The Cluny Museum

Alain Erlande-Brandenburg
Chief Curator of the Cluny Museum

Ministère de la Culture

Éditions de la Réunion des Musées Nationaux

MUSEUMS OF THE ROMAN BATHS AND THE HOTEL DE CLUNY
6, PLACE PAUL PAINLEVÉ 75005 PARIS Tél. 990.04.04.

I.S.B.N. 2-7118-0113-6

© Editions de la Réunion des Musées Nationaux
10, rue de l'Abbaye - 75006 PARIS - 1983

THE CLUNY MUSEUM

The "Musée des Thermes" and the "Hôtel de Cluny" have the rare merit of being two buildings that have a very close link with the collections exhibited in them. This link is not fortuitous, but the result of a plan that has taken a little more than a century to carry out completely. The Gallo-Roman baths were an ideal place to house the great masterpieces of ancient Paris; and the Gothic house of the Cluny abbots was a perfect setting for one of the world's richest collections of mediaeval art. It was not until the museum was re-organized after the Second World War that this link could be finally and entirely achieved.

THE BATHS

THE BUILDING

The Gallo-Roman baths form one of the most impressive monuments that survive from the ancient civilization that existed where Paris stands today. Lutetia, as it was then called, was really two towns: one was on the Ile de la Cité, and it was surrounded by a city wall in the Vth Century; the second, founded by the Roman conquerors on the Montagne Sainte-Geneviève, was on the slopes descending towards the Seine. They were separated by the majestic river and by a marshy area which extended up to the line of the present Boulevard Saint-Germain. The ancient monuments were to the South: the forum, under the rue Soufflot; the Southern baths, close by; the Eastern baths under the Collège de France and the Northern baths at the point where the present Boulevards Saint-Germain and Saint-Michel cross.

Built on the hillside sloping gently down towards the Seine, the ancient building was constructed on beaten earth towards the South, and over a basement to the North to compensate for the sloping site. The architect designed it as a long rectangle (323 ft. long x 210 ft. wide). It is thus similar in dimension to the Cherchel baths in Algeria, but is considerably smaller than those at Trier (550 ft. x 320 ft.).

The excavations carried out during the XIXth Century under the careful supervision of Théodore Vacquer, and after the Second World War by Mr Paul-Marie Duval, have made it possible to reconstitute the original plan and arrangements. The three rooms — the *Frigidarium*, which still survives in its entirety, the *Tepidarium* and the *Caldarium*, both in ruins – lead one out of the other, as was normal. Another room, which is today occupied by rooms VIII and IX of the museum, was originally heated and probably served as a meeting room. The palaestras were to the West and to the East, on either side of the *Frigidarium*. The building, which was constructed all in one piece in small bricks (known as "pastoureaux") separated by regular courses of tie-bricks, dates from the last quarter of the IInd century or the first quarter of the IIIrd. The brick pattern, which is today so attractive through its quality, regularity and colour contrast, was hidden by rendering covered by a marble decor. The presence in the Frigidarium, under the spring of the arches, of corbels in the form of the prow of a ship laden with equipment shows that the building was financed by the generosity of the powerful corporation of the "Nautes", the Paris boatmen.

THE HOUSE OF THE ABBOTS OF CLUNY

It was in this city, abandoned following the barbarian invasions, that
the University was set up during the XIIIth Century, forming what
came to be called the "Latin Quarter". The powerful abbots of Cluny
bought several houses there alongside the Thermal Baths, and they
had the use of a hanging garden over the ancient vaults. They made
this their Paris lodging when they came on visits from Burgundy.
At the end of the XVth Century, the abbot Jacques d'Amboise (1485-
1510), whose brothers were well known for their munificence as art
patrons, had built there a house that fitted better his taste for osten-
tation, and this soon came to be known as the "Palace of Amboise".
It is built on a U-shaped plan: there is a main wing to the north.
with two smaller side wings built out from each end; they are linked
to the South by a wall with battlements, which once had a sentry
walk on it. There was thus an internal courtyard. Towards the North
is another wing which includes a room and a chapel. this is one of

the first examples of a house built between a courtyard and a garden —
a pattern that was to become very popular in the XVIIth century in
Paris and in the major provincial cities.

The objects in the museum's inventory are of various origins; three of these origins were especially important, and it is they that have given the present museum its character: the collections of Alexandre Du Sommerard, the stone-work collection of the city of Paris, and lastly the acquisitions made after the creation of the museum. Today, the inventory has 22,888 entries.

ALEXANDRE DU SOMMERARD

Born in 1771 at Bar-sur-Aube, Alexandre Du Sommerard entered on a career as a soldier at a very early age, before joining the staff of the Cour des Comptes (State Audit Office) in 1807 as Chief Clerk; he ended his career there as Principal Adviser. At a time when the Middle Ages and Renaissance periods were little appreciated or even despised, and the cult of the antique held sway, he developed a keen interest for these later periods. He soon appeared as a precursor in this speciality, and his curiosity extended to many other fields. To illustrate a vast work on the *"Arts in the Middle Ages"*, published in five volumes (1838-1846) he made use of a recent process that was still in its early stages of development: lithography. With this, he reproduced a large number of the objects in his collection, as well as others. Following the example of the "antiquaries" as they were then known — Debruge-Duménil, Revoil, Sauvageot and many others — he acquired objects some of which are recognized today as great masterpieces. In order to pay for these purchases, he had to dispose, in 1826, of a valuable series of old and modern drawings. His collection soon became famous in Paris; he liked to move in society and literary circles, and was free with his invitations to visit it. In 1825, at a time when he was still living in the rue des Menus, a picture of him entitled "The Antiquary", by Xavier Leprince, shows him in the middle of his precious objects. Their growing number soon made it necessary to move house and his choice, which proved a fortunate one, fell on the house of the Abbots of Cluny. Like Alexandre Lenoir, he had the

imagination to exploit the setting and to present his treasures in a way that must have impressed his visitors. Engravings and paintings show the care with which Du Sommerard placed his objects on show. With an amazing sense of theatre, he evoked the memory of famous men. François I, whom Sauvageot used to call "his king", was especially glorified: he was given a room, in which were his bed, his stirrups and many other objects generously attributed to him. Elsewhere, there was an extraordinary mixture of technique and period, with the most diverse objects associated together without any chronological link, most of them being attached to some illustrious origin. Some of these objects were less authentic than Du Sommerard believed, while others have proved — especially certain articles of furniture — to be curious creations in which good original wood panels were placed alongside others made for the occasion. There

were forgeries in the middle of this vast array of bric-a-brac, at a time when authenticity criticism was in its infancy and when clever forgers had no difficulty in taking advantage of a purchaser's good faith.

Du Sommerard's contemporaries, who were conscious of the link that had become established between this collection and the building in which it was housed, expressed the desire that this link should become indissoluble through the creation of a museum. In 1833, Albert Lenoir, who was the son of the founder of the Museum of French Monuments, showed in his salon a "Project for a historical museum to be formed by joining up the Palais des Thermes and the Hôtel de Cluny". This idea met with considerable enthusiasm, which was reinforced by the fact that the city of Paris had set up a deposit of stone-work in the *Frigidarium* room in the baths.

THE CITY STONE-WORK DEPOSIT

The Gallo-Roman baths, which were proclaimed national property under the Revolution, had not found a purchaser. They were disposed of in 1809 to the Charenton home for the sick. Even before this time, the "antiquomaniacs" had become concerned for their conservation and for their being put to a better use. In 1807 Baltard expressed the wish that the *Frigidarium* should be emptied and that there should be placed there "the sculptures executed or at least brought there by the Romans in Paris". In 1809 Grivaud brought up again the idea of creating a museum, as did later Quatremère de Quincy in 1817. The closing in 1816 of the French Museum of Historic Monuments created under the Revolution by Alexandre Lenoir was to reinforce this current of opinion, which derived additional backing from the need to find a place for the sculptures that had formerly been exhibited there. Alexandre Lenoir himself was an earnest protagonist for this idea, hoping that he could thus revive his former museum project. Under this pressure, Louis XVIII in 1819 ordered the ruins to be purchased, the baths to be cleared and a curator to be appointed, who moved the ancient sculptures there. The state quickly lost interest in the affair, and the city of Paris took it over in 1836. It felt that it, like the other great cities in the kingdom, should have its "museum of Gallic and Roman antiquities". It quickly lodged there a number of sculptures originating from the demolition or restoration of buildings in Paris, or even from excavations. The success of this initiative was linked with the hope that the Du Sommerard collections in the house next door would soon become national property.

The death of the famous collector, on August 19th 1842, was to accelerate this process. By astute negotiations, the city persuaded the state to buy the Thermal Baths and the stone-work collections subject to the condition that Edmond, the son of Alexandre, should be appointed curator. On July Ist, the Chambre des Députés approved by vote the purchase of the house and the collections. The creation of the "Musée des Thermes et de l'Hôtel de Cluny" was authorized by the law of July 24th 1843: Edmond Du Sommerard was appointed curator and

Albert Lenoir, architect. During the long debates that preceded this decision, the former French Museum of Monuments was frequently mentioned. Its memory was always present as a shade to which it was hoped new life could be given, but it also provoked feelings of remorse, as its closure had caused considerable emotion. The opening was a triumphal occasion. On March 17th 1844, there were 12,000 visitors, and on the following Sunday 16,000. The merger of the two collections of widely differing origins was to give the museum an atmosphere that it still retains, one of extraordinary variety. The city donated the capitals from Saint-Germain-des-Prés, the statues of Notre Dame that were discovered in 1839 in the rue de la Santé, and the ancient fragments that were formerly in the French Museum for Historic Monuments: the altar of the Paris boatmen, and the bull of Saint-Marcel. The second group included 1,434 objects from the Du Sommerard collection which were distributed among the 19 rooms that were then open. On the same occasion, the public was introduced to two wonderful buildings: the Gallo-Roman Thermal Baths and the Hôtel de Jacques d'Amboise.

The appointment of Edmond Du Sommerard as curator of this wealth of objects was to prove a fortunate one. At his death in 1889, after 40 years of management, he left a catalogue that had 10,351 entries. It is he that we should recognize as the true creator of the museum. His first preoccupation was to bring order to his father's collections, and in his first catalogue that appeared in 1847 he adopted a classification based on the different productions of art and industry. Within each of these sections, the objects were disposed in chronological order; the collector had finally and permanently made way for the expert. He then set about reorganizing the rooms, which up to the Second World War retained a character that recalled their creation during the XIXth Century. In so doing he succeeded in establishing the Museum of National Antiquities whose creation had been so fervently desired.

As it was under the authority of the High Commission for Historical Monuments, it was able to acquire a large number of architectural and sculptural fragments originating from restorations (the apostles of the Sainte-Chapelle) or from destruction (the chapel of the College of Cluny). To these stone-work collections were added plaster casts, forming a nucleus for the future museum of comparative sculpture, which has since become the French Museum of Historical Monuments. Du Sommerard extended the exhibition area to the garden that had just been laid out by order of Napoleon III, and he made this a section of the museum by setting up elements of architecture, sculptures and plaster casts under the young trees. The famous Elysée garden of the French Museum of Historical Monuments thus made a timid reappearance. The curator's tireless energy was also devoted to purchasing activities. Always on the lookout for the possibility of a sale, he lost no opportunity to obtain new objects for his museum and it is he who acquired for it its greatest masterpieces. At Rouen, he bought the six tapestries of *"la Vie Seigneuriale"*, following his purchase at Genoa of the ten Brussels pieces of the *"History of David"* series, which there is nothing to match in the other French museums for their dimensions and their beauty. When the Hôtel-Dieu at Auxerre decided to sell the cathedral tapestries he immediately persuaded the commission and the ministry to acquire them for Cluny. And finally he negotiated with the municipality of Boussac to purchase the famous *"Lady with the Unicorn"* set when it had decided to dispose of it. He enriched the gold and silver collection with several unique pieces: the golden crowns of the Vizigoth kings, which had been found by a French officer living in Spain; the famous relics from the treasure of Basle cathedral, the altar that

had been given by the Emperor Henry II and the golden rose, both of which had been sold by the Canton of Basle and bought by a private collector. His acquisitions were no less remarkable in other fields: sculpture (six stone fireplaces), ceramics (three large medallions by the della Robbia), painting and enamelwork, to say nothing of the collections of illustrated lead counters that had been found in the Seine river.

After him, Alfred Darcel principally concerned himself with reviving the collections, removing imitations, dismantling composite pieces of furniture — projects that his predecessor, out of respect for his father, had dared not undertake.

In 1907 the museum was transferred from the Commission for Historic Monuments and came under the administration of the National museums. Edmond Haraucourt, a poet and man of letters, became its director; his principal contribution was to increase considerably the number of catalogued works by placing on display many objects that had been placed in the reserves.

After him, J.J. Marquet de Vasselot undertook a massive work reorganization, eliminating numbers of objects that had been out of place there, and rearranging the others in line with current display ideas. Thus, he devoted an entire room to the magnificent woodwork from the chapel at Gaillon.

The closure in 1939 of the Cluny museum was to mark the end of an epoch that of the 19th — century museum, which had been in existence for nearly a century. It was to begin on a new destiny as soon as hostilities ended.

THE PRESENT MUSEUM

During the war, the works had to be transferred to a place of safety. When peace returned it was agreed that substantial architectural works were necessary, and that the presentation of the collection should be redesigned. Account had to be taken of public demand, for whose taste far too many objects were on display in too small an area. It was therefore decided to present the ancient sculpture in the Gallo-Roman Thermal Baths, and the antiques from the Middle ages in the 15th century house.

These very varied collections had to be made to comply with the demands of a building whose intrinsic qualities commanded respect. Lastly, the Thermal Baths room, which is the finest ancient civilization left on the soil of France, required presentation on its own account. So as not to encumber a place of such striking beauty, no more than a few sculptures found in Paris and of the same date could be exhibited there. The same applied to the chapel, a precious reminder of the final period of flamboyant architecture in the centre of Paris. The objects were distributed among the 24 exhibition rooms.

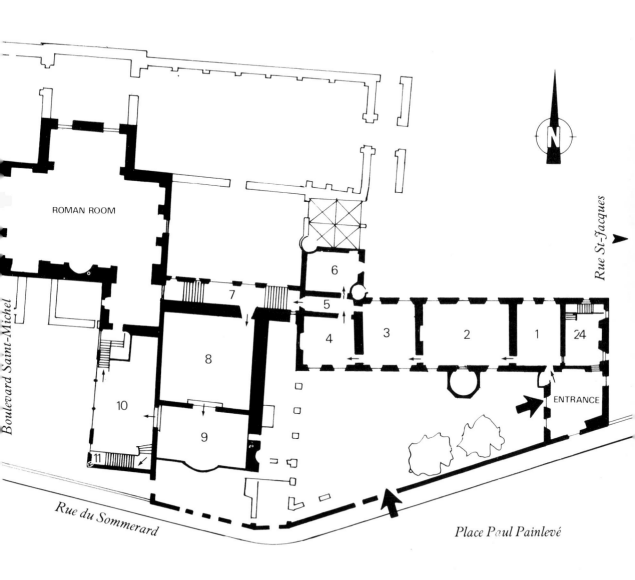

Boulevard Saint-Germain

ROMAN ROOM

Boulevard Saint-Michel

Rue St-Jacques

6

7

5

4   3   2   1   24

8

10

9

11

ENTRANCE

Rue du Sommerard

Place Paul Painlevé

PLAN OF THE GROUND FLOOR

ROOM 1

The entry to the museum is through the former kitchens of the house of the Cluny abbots. The only surviving momento of its vocation is a magnificent stone fireplace whose mantle has a sculptured keystone representing the Trinity. It comes from the convent of the Trinity at Jativa, in Spain.

Costume. Intrinsically fragile, it has rarely survived, and what still exists was usually found in tombs. Thus to reconstitute what was worn at the time we have to fall back on illustrations: illuminated manuscripts, paintings, tapestries or sculptures, taking into account the period of time that elapsed between the appearance of a fashion and the date when it was illustrated, and also the artist's inventive licence.

SHOES

However leather, which is less fragile and was produced in considerable quantities during the Middle Ages, has been better preserved. Many shoes have been found in tombs, certain in a state of remarkable preservation. During work carried out in Paris between 1923 and 1927 on the site of the present-day church dedicated to Notre-Dame de Bonne-Nouvelle, there were found a shoe for the right foot, the uppers of a shoe for the left foot and a shoe buckle; these are in the showcase to the right of the door *(1)*. They are probably XIVth and XVth centuries.

To the left of this door there is a second showcase *(2)* which also contains two soles, one for the left and the other for the right foot, which are very pointed as was the fashion at the end of the XIVth century; here also can be seen an upper in soft leather with an openwork pattern of diamonds with toothed sides. These three pieces come from the same excavation. The boot sole, whose square toe shows that it is of a later period, was discovered in the convent of el Coblet in Spain in the tomb of king Alfonso V, who died in 1458. The man's shoe

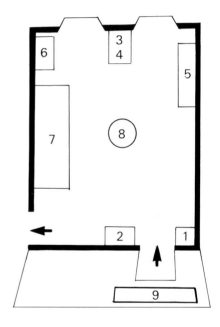

2

6

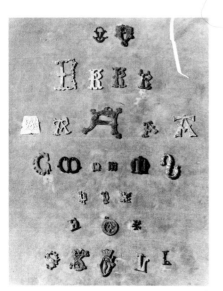

5

with rounded toe comes from the end of this century; the fashion is known as "bear's foot", and many examples of it are to be seen in contemporary manuscripts and tapestries.

COSTUME ACCESSORIES

There was a great variety of costume accessories during the Middle Ages, as this showcase *(3)*, where a large number of them have been assembled, bears witness. Most come from the collection that Victor Gay patiently put together throughout his lifetime before leaving them to the museum. They are made in a number of different materials; some are in cheap lead, and were sewn onto belts as ornamental trinkets. At the time they took the form of letters, fleurs de lys or even of alms-purses. There were studs too. Other ornaments were in cast bronze, for instance purse mountings, belt pendants and buckles, small chains, clips and clasps. The artisans who made them liked to add a delicate decoration, like this Annonciation within the circle of a pendant.

CASKETS

Caskets, cases or book covers were also frequently found, made in a variety of materials. Some were in metal (see room XXII). Others, such as the three caskets and one case *(4)* shown here were in leather. One casket has a metal mount, and another has a domed lid. The third, also with a domed lid, is chased with scenes, including one of a unicorn hunt. Lastly, the book cover has an elegant tooled decoration.

cabinet 3

A casket here is chased with endlessly-repeating couples, and the inside of it shows an engraved Virgin and Child. There is a fine goblet case

3

6

bearing its owner's coat of arms, which has not yet been identified. Another case is in the form of a saddle holster, and has seven compartments; it is embossed with a nativity scene and four figures of saints; the arms of a king are stamped on its lid, and those of the city of Dijon on its back *(5)*.

cabinet 4 *(6)*

These different objects are as diverse in their shapes as in their origins. The long casket with domed back chased with an animal decoration is probably XIVth-century Spanish. The large casket in the form of a house on which are engraved scenes from romances or from the life of Christ, and also the casket that has the initials MC engraved on its domed lid are XIVth-century Italian.

WOOD

The large wooden chest *(7)*, which is a stable chest, is just as unusual in its dimensions as in its decoration of arcaded ironwork; it probably dates from the 1300s. It was probably used to contain oats for the horses. In the middle of the room there is an extraordinary pillar *(8)* which carries at its end the arms of the priory of Saint-Pierre-le-Moûtier (Nièvre), held up by an angel. It is said to come from the capitular room. Above the door that communicates with the next room there is a marvellous Annonciation, carved in fine walnut; this was the work of a German artist at the beginning of the XVIth century.

8

The concert

TAPESTRY

The museum is proud to own one of the finest collections of Middle-Ages tapestry. The archive documents tell us how extraordinarily rich this production was, but only certain relics have come down to us. The *Resurrection (9)* which is woven with silk and metal thread is a work of great preciousness, due to the fact that it was intended as an altar hanging. It is early-XIVth-century, and is the museum's most sumptuous tapestry.

1

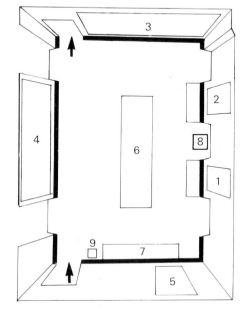

This room is specially devoted to tapestry. Some of the works are from the first third of the XVth century and others are dated around 1500.

The *Offering of the Heart (1)* is with the Resurrection one of the earliest hangings in the museum. Woven in wool, it shows against a background of dark blue verdure a man who advances to offer his heart to a seated woman. The elegance of the figures and the very-freely treated costume suggests the international Gothic style of 1400s; this tapestry is one of its last manifestations.

The *Delivery of Saint Peter (2)* comes from a very large hanging that was given by the bishop of Beauvais, Guillaume de Hellande, to his cathedral. It shows the arms of the cathedral chapter, and also those of the donor together with his adopted motto *"peace"*. The other pieces in this set are still in the cathedral, or dispersed in private collections, or again in American museums. The style of the drawing is still characterized by the use of very soft fabrics which, a few years later, were to adopt broken pleats.

The *Miracle of Saint Quentin (3)* is a choir hanging which probably comes from the basilica of Saint-Quentin, in the North of France. It illustrates a miracle performed by the saint, the legend of which is related, on the lines of a strip cartoon, in a long inscription in the Picardy dialect.

The *Grape Harvest (4)* shows two scenes that are largely realistic: on the left, treading the grapes, and on the right picking them. The third scene, on the extreme right, has unfortunately been cut. The arms of the owner and of his wife that are woven into the upper corners have not yet been identified.

PAINTING

5

A panel painted on oak illustrates on one side the episode of *Saint Joseph's Flowering Rod*, and on the other side, against a black background, the *Arma Christi* (instruments of Christ's Passion). This painting, which dates from around 1470, is today attributed to a Dutch painter who was probably working in Burgundy *(5)*.

The function of the folding table *(6)* in the middle of the room is uncertain; it is in fact not sure that it was a table at all, and could have been a non-religious folding painting on the lines of an altarpiece, whose flaps could be opened and shut at will. The painting is by a German artist from the middle of the XIVth century, and is in a remarkable state of preservation. Around the border are coats of arms identified by inscriptions that list the principal provinces and cities of the Holy Roman Empire. In the middle, alternating with coats of arms and topped by plumed helmets, are four quatrefoils on which are scenes whose meaning is sometimes obscure. From left to right, the legend of the Golden Ass of Apuleus, an oriental proverb, the flight of a bird through the air, the movement of a snake over the ground, that of a ship over the sea and finally youth: all these defy interpretation; there follows the legend of *Barlaam and Jehoshaphat (?)*, and lastly the *Judgment of Solomon*.

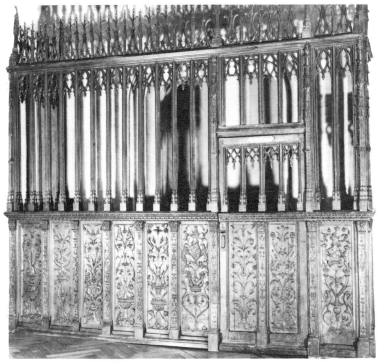

7

9

8

WOOD

The beautiful choir-screen of the church of Augerolles (Puy-de-Dôme) has been set up against the wall; it is from the beginning of the XVIth century, and is a remarkably happy mixture of the flamboyant style in its fenestrated parts and early Renaissance in its panelling (7).

SCULPTURE

Between the windows is a very lovely head from the reclining statue of Jeanne of Toulouse, the wife of Alphonse de Poitiers and the brother of saint Louis, who died in 1271 on his return from the Tunis crusade. Philip the Bold in 1280 ordered a funeral effigy from a Parisian artist, which was placed in the abbey church of Gercy (Essonne). Only the head has been found (8).

Another statue shows the erect figure of a swineherd of about 1500, with his characteristic dress and equipment: stick, cloak, scrip, barrel, etc. (9).

ROOM III

WEAVERS AND EMBROIDERERS

One of the most active trades in the Middle Ages, alongside that in gold
and silver plate, was the cloth trade. But, while certain facts are well
known: that Byzantium silks were highly sought after in the Carolingian epoch, Italian silks were principally admired during the XVth
century, that the cloth merchants occupied a very important position
in the great fairs of the Champagne area, and that the wool merchants
brought enormous riches to the cities of Flanders, it is more difficult
to determine the exact origin and place of manufacture of many
of the examples of fabric that have come down to us.

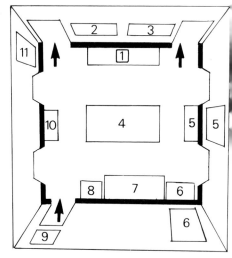

The French embroiderers were far from the leading exponents of their
trade in the Middle Ages. In England and in the Rhineland there
existed, during the XIVth century, two centres of European reputation, to the extent that the phrases *"opus anglicanum"* (made in
England) and *"opus coloniense"* (made at Cologne) became synony-
mous with sought-after embroidery.

On the wall opposite the entrance to the room, on either side of a wooden
statue — a *pope (1)* from the beginning of the XIVth century, on which
one can still see, under the worn coloured decoration, the base
covering of coarse cloth — there are two large embroidered panels:
one from the XIIIth century, which shows the *Life and Miracles of
Saint Martin (2)*, is an embroidery that was done in Iceland; the
composition in the form of medallion shows the influence of French
stained glass; the other, from the first half of the XVth century,
is a fine *altar hanging (3),* which was donated in 1889 by Baron Adolphe
de Rothschild and can be considered as an "opus coloniense";
on a yellow background picked out in silver and uncker architectural
canopies are shown episodes from the lives of Saint Mark and Saint
John.

cabinet 1 — IN THE MIDDLE OF THE ROOM *(4)*

In the middle of the cabinet are three bishop's *mitres*. One, a mourning
mitre from the last third of the XIVth century, bears drawing in

black on white silk; the comparison is obvious with the Narbonne frontal in the Louvre. It is said to come from the Sainte Chapelle in Paris, as is also the large embroidered mitre made in about 1400. The third, which dates from the end of the XIVth century, was in the Du Sommerard collection, though nothing more is known about its origin.

This cabinet also contains, among the French pieces, a XIIIth-century embroidered *corporalier,* a beautiful *Burgundian panel* from the same period and two *alms-purses* (which, in the Middle Ages, were in a way the equivalent of womens' handbags), which were perhaps made in Paris during the XIVth century; among the German pieces are two *Evangelists* in a very marked Romanesque style and an *alms-purse* with a geometric line in beautiful colours; among the Italian pieces are two panels showing consummate technique: A *Miracle* and a *Saint Christopher.*

4

3

cabinet and panel 2 between the windows on the garden side *(5).*

The Marcel Guérin legacy has recently enriched Cluny with a collection of fabrics assembled by this discerning amateur collector. They have been kept together in a cabinet containing many drawers; only the fabrics of Coptic origin, i.e., woven in Egypt between the IVth and Xth century of our era and found in tombs, have been placed on the wall and above the cabinet. The attraction of these little tapestries is in their bright colours (the fabric with a bird motif) or in their design (the lion).

cabinet and panel 3 to the right of the window overlooking the garden *(6)*

The court of Byzantium, at the gates of the Orient, provided silk weavers with an enormous amount of activity. Some of the most sumptuous fabrics that have ever been made came from the imperial ateliers. Throughout the first centuries of the Middle Ages, there was never any question of their superiority in the Western world. Many of these fabrics were found in tombs or reliquaries, but nearly all are in a

6

fragmentary state. It is a rare thing to discover, as did some years ago the clergy of Reims cathedral and the department of Historical Monuments, a shroud in such good condition as that of Saint Rémi.

There are a number of very beautiful specimens here: for instance, the large piece of blue fabric showing a four-horse chariot that comes from the treasure of Aix-la-Chapelle, the striking fragment on which is repeated the silhouette of Samson opening the lion's mouth against a red background, or again the tiny piece showing Amazons. All were woven at Byzantium or in some other province of the empire between the VIth and IXth century.

cabinet 4 ITALIAN FABRICS *(7)*

Byzantian influence affected Italy either directly or more usually through Moslem visitors from Sicily and Spain. The designs of monsters, birds, lions affrontee (facing each other), and circular borders were taken up in Italy and in time became deformed or transformed.

Siena, Lucca and Florence were, in the XIVth and XVth centuries, the major centres in Europe where beautiful silks were made. It is often difficult to distinguish between these three centres. On these fabrics, even when they are worn, one can appreciate the taste of the weaver who knew how to use gold thread without excess.

The Italians in the Middle Ages also worked in velvet, with a success that made them worthy rivals of their Eastern counterparts: Florence, Genoa and Venice produced splendid fabrics, such as a fine piece of blue velvet from the XVth century here exhibited; it is a remarkable example, but only one among many.

4

6

28

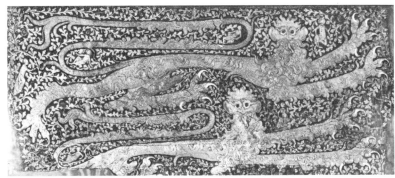

cabinet 5 — SPANISH AND HISPANO-MOORISH FABRICS *(8)*

The Moslems also introduced silk weaving into Spain. Some Hispano-Moorish cloths are very similar to Arab workmanship from Sicily; others are quite different.

They were woven in countries under Arab domination or in kingdoms that had remained Christian but had been considerably influenced by Moslem art; and a factor common to all is their richness and sumptuousness. A fragment on display here comes from the tomb of a XIIIth-century Christian prince, who was a friend of the emir of Granada. Noteworthy also are two brightly-coloured embroideries, which were no doubt worked under Moslem rule at the end of the Middle Ages. The magnificent piece of purplish-blue silk worked in Arabic characters is also a good example of the production from ateliers in Spain, which were principally active at Seville and Granada.

Above is an embroidery in gold on red velvet that may originally have been from a horse-cloth, reworked in the XVIIIth century into a chasuble; it shows the leopards of England. This is a work from the beginning of the XIVth century, probably English *(9)*.

cabinet 6 — BORDERS *(10)*

The orphreys or embroidered borders that can be seen at the back of this cabinet and which were generally used to edge chasubles and copes should be considered as works from Cologne.
The texts found by Gay show that orphreys were also made in France, Rome and in Paris, "de opere parisiensi".
Lastly, on the wall close to the next room, is a delicate XIIIth-century embroidery from Burgundy, containing gold thread, which is in an admirable state of preservation *(11)*.

ROOM IV

LIFE IN THE GREAT HOUSES

We have tried to reconstitute a mediaeval room using an area that was particularly suitable for this. There is a string mat on the floor. A fireplace *(1)* from a house at Le Mans dating from the beginning of the XVth century, as is shown by the costumes of the figures on the mantlepiece, has been installed. Two chests *(2)*, an octagonal table *(3)* which can easily be dismantled and so transported, and lastly a dresser *(4)* constitute the essential of the furnishings. The lords of the manor used to display their gold or silver plate on dressers, the number of steps in them showing the rank of their owners. In the absence of such precious plate, we have shown here some enamelware made in Venice at the beginning of the XVIth century. Its blue colour makes an agreeable contrast with the white enamel picked out in gold or torquoise.

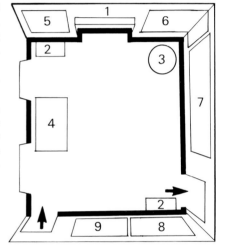

THE TAPESTRY SET

The tapestry set known as "La Vie seigneuriale", which was bought in 1852 from a noble family in Rouen, is composed of six pieces: *Embroidery (5), Reading (6), the Walk (7), the Departure for the Hunt (8), the Bath (9)* and *Scenes of Gallantry;* for lack of room, this last piece is exhibited in room VI.

As the general title, which was given to the set in the XIXth century, and the subject matter of each of the pieces suggest, the tapestries evoke the activities of a lord and his lady of about the year 1500.

Like the *"Concert"* in room I, this set, which is woven in wool, is an example of the "mille-fleurs" technique. The background, which is generally dark blue, is dotted with tiny flowering plants, with a few trees and animals of every kind. The characters are lost in this luxuriance of vegetation, and are juxtaposed without any real link between them: they never look at each other and their feet are not on the ground – and in fact there is none. This very special way of working was in fact an economy measure, as it is known that the weaver reused the cartons which were the basis for his design, modifying

4

3

7

8

them slightly if need be. There is an example of this here in the serving girl who is shown firstly in *"the Bath"*, and secondly in *"the Walk"*. The figures can be superimposed one over the other, but there are a few variations which shows how the weaver was careful to break the uniformity: the changes are mainly in the colours of the clothes and in the hairstyles. He was able to draw his inspiration from the work of the principal artists of his time: the halberdier in *"Departure for the Hunt"* is taken from a Dürer engraving: the *Six Warriors*, dated 1495 to 1496. The same engraving also served as inspiration for the *"Miracle of Saint Julian"* in the Louvre, and for a tapestry with pink background in the Art Institute of Chicago. This diversity of inspiration sources is paralleled in the style. In *"the Bath"*, a superb young lady is shown naked in a bath tub decorated with acanthus flowers, which already shows the influence of Renaissance art, whereas the draperies whose sharp folds break on the ground are characteristic of the art of the Southern Netherlands at the end of the XVth century.

ROOM V

WOODWORK
CARPENTRY

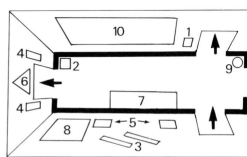

The artisans of the Middle Ages were skilled in making all kinds of things from wood, both as carpenters and in the finer art of cabinet-making.

The carpenters cut, shaped, assembled and set up timberwork, using cutting instruments like this iron axe from the XVth century *(1)*, which was found in the Loire river. The timberwork was composed of a succession of trusses (horizontal pieces) supported by king posts (vertical pieces) which were often decorated at the bottom and top. The base *(2)* and the two exposed capitals remain as precious evidence of a decoration that most people never saw. The timberwork could carry mouldings, when it was visible, like the two rafters *(3)* which acted as trusses and are shown on the South wall; they come from the hôtel de Cluny. The woodwork was supported on corbels that take the most varied forms, such as for instance these *(4)* which were carved at the beginning of the XVth century in the form of human heads; they are above the door which leads out into corridor VII.

10

The carpenters described as "de grande cognée" (literally, big-axe carpenters) did other kinds of woodwork: the two arcature fragments from the end of the XVth century *(5)* (South wall), and the early-XVIth-century gable *(6)* (West wall) are examples of this, but they also made church stalls. The three presented here *(7)* are a XIXth-century assembly in which only the parcloses – the partitions separating the seats – and the "misericords" are of the period. Above them, a carved inscription *Si qua fata Sinant* (if destiny allows) comes from Lausanne cathedral.

In an opening that is today blocked up a window with internal shutters has been set up; it is from the XVth century *(8)*; and in a niche there is a standing female saint *(9)* whose style already presages the Renaissance.

A fragment of tapestry has been hung on the North wall; its subject matter is still obscure *(10)*.

ROOM VI

WOODWORK
CABINETMAKING

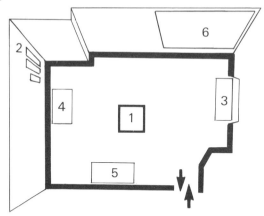

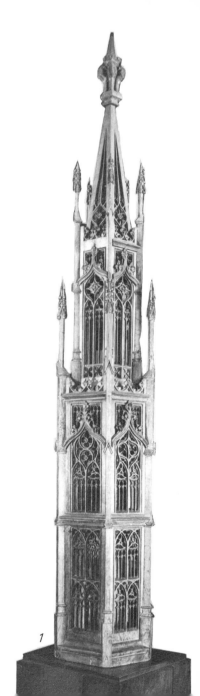

It was not until the XVth century that the carpenters' guilds broke up
into "heavy-axe" and "light-axe" carpenters; the latter, because of
the fineness of their work, gradually took on the name of "menuisier"
("menu", in French, means small); this is the name generally given
today to cabinet-makers. This semantic change was the consequence
of technical progress. Initially, furniture was made of planks of wood,
squared off and roughly planed, later, it was formed of a frame assembled with tenons and mortices, in which panels carved in bas-relief
were matched.

The wooden tabernacle *(1)* in the middle of the room is a work of unusual
delicacy; the craftsman took as his model for it a church tower with
its abutments ending in pinnacles. The decoration of the bays is a
transposition into wood of the patterns used in stone architecture
during the flamboyant period.

The furniture was made up of mounted panels which show extraordinary
decorative invention. Evidence of this can be found in the examples
presented on the walls of this room. The decoration in inlays and
fillets has been carved very freely in relief. On the west wall, to the
right, there are three panels *(2)* of unusual beauty; they were made
at the beginning of the XVth century by Jean de Liège for the stall
of the officiating priests at the Carthusian monastry of Champmol,
on the outskirts of Dijon.

1

3

4

6

5

General-use chests, like this one with a rounded lid *(3)*, were used for travelling. The one here still has its covering of leather, with fittings of iron fastened by nails, and is a rare surviving example of an object of which there are many descriptions in the contemporary texts. Another furnishing chest *(4)* is decorated on its front with an extraordinary tournament scene, carved in bas-relief; it shows the various stages of a XVth-century joust. In Italy, the furniture was more elaborate, like this small chest *(5)* from the end of the XVth century; its marquetry in a variety of woods and bone shows, on its front, three vases and a geometrical decoration on its cover and sides, of the type known as "certosina"; another example of this style is this X-shaped chair from the same period, on which we find the same technique.

Furniture decoration was often confined to panels described as "pleated napkin" or "pleated parchment", of which many examples survive. The *Arithmetic* tapestry *(6)* portrays an example of this: the young woman is doing her accounts on a desk decorated in this fashion. This piece was originally a part of a hanging illustrating liberal arts.

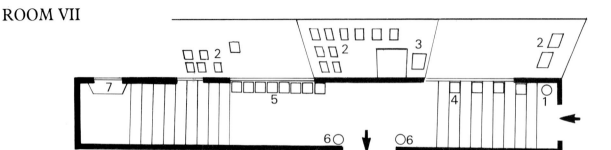

The corridor communicates between the house of the Cluny abbots and the Gallo-Roman baths whose floor level is much lower. Shown here are a number of sculptures, including an angel *(1)* which was originally one of a pair with an Annunciation Virgin. This wooden statue, which still has some traces of polychrome, came from the XIVth-century atelier of Nino Pisano, who probably took his inspiration from the one in the church of Saint Catherine at Pisa.

We also have here a number of XVth-century alabasters *(2)*, which illustrate the extensive production of Nottingham in England, which approached a semi-industrial scale. It had inundated the Continent, where generally only isolated panels have survived. Originally these were painted and gilded and formed immense altar screens. They have been presented here by theme, the better to emphasize the similarities and differences of subject. The Saint Ursula *(3)* to the right of the door holds in her hand the arrow of her martyrdom and shelters her eleven thousand companions under her ample cloak.

The four romanesque capitals *(4)* are eloquent examples or romanesque sculpture in the Ile-de-France. The second, which is decorated with wide palm-leaf mouldings, comes from the church of Saint-Martins-des-Champs in Paris, whereas the last, which was one of a twin, is magnificently carved with a lion and a winged mermaid; before this church's demolition, it formed part of the decoration of Notre-Dame at Corbeil.

The eight other capitals *(5)* illustrate the development of Gothic floral decoration from the middle of the XIIth-century to that of the following one: from the water-lily clinging to the basket, via a hooked design, to the flower pervading it entirely. The two other isolated capitals *(6)*, mounted on columns and set up either side of the door, probably came from Maubuisson: the branches of may blossom that decorate them have been carved with rare delicacy.

1

2

3

7

At the foot of the step we find an altarpiece *(7)* that came from the church of Champdeuil (Seine-et-Marne); it is devoted to the life of Christ. The style of the work dates it from the first third of the XVIth-century, and suggests that it is a local production deriving inspiration from an altar screen at Antwerp. The shutters, signed by Lucas Loïs, are probably of Spanish origin.

ROOM VIII

PAINTING AND SCULPTURE

This large room has partly retained its original proportions and aspect: though the floor level has been considerably raised, and a modern vault has replaced at the same height that destroyed in 1737, and while a wall has been built to the south where there was formerly a large arch communicating with the next room, the other walls are original, that to the west having suffered considerable deterioration with the passage of the centuries, and the other two still with their niches or windows which have been restored in recent works.

In this room are assembled works of painters and sculptors, the image-makers of the end of the Middle Ages; this is by no means an arbitrary association, because at the time there was scarcely any difference between the two trades.

As representatives of the XIVth century, it will be of no surprise to find here several representations of the Virgin and Child: statues of this type were made at the time in such numbers that they still abound in the churches of France and in the museums of the whole world. On either side of the large bay in the south wall we find a beautiful stone Virgin (1) in the style of Lorraine, and another in marble (2) which comes from the abbey of the Dames-de-Longchamps. In group I, the same subject has been treated in wood (3) by a sculptor from Liège. Next to this statue is a French Virgin (4) whose stone still has attractive polychrome painting, and another in marble (5) which used to be in the Hospice de Sens. The theme of the seated Virgin (6), which is met with less frequently than that of the standing Virgin, is represented here in the corner of the group by a work whose quality has scarcely been affected by the accidents it has suffered. In the centre of this collection is the most distinguished group of sculptures that the museum has from this period, the *Presentation in the Temple (7)* which is carved in marble. This same grouping contains several works that are representative of marble or alabaster, for instance the pieces of the *Ascent to Calvary (8)* and of the *Entomb-*

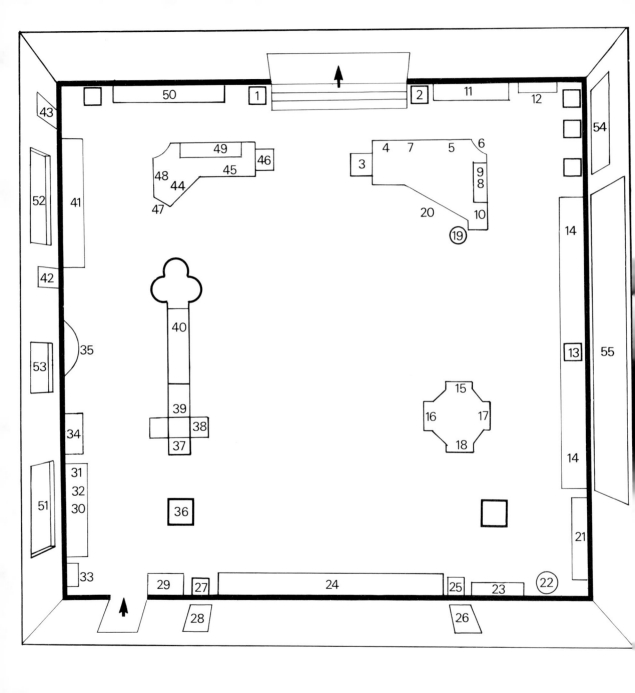

1
2
5
11
6

7

ment (9). Alongside is an ivory Virgin *(10),* one of the largest that has ever been carved from an elephant tusk; it is representative of the work of the ivory-carvers.

cabinet I

Cabinet I *(11)* is entirely devoted to such work: lay objects whose subjects have been taken from contemporary romances are shown alongside religious objects, the most beautiful of which, despite certain alterations, is still the triptych from Saint-Sulpice-du-Tarn, which was probably made in an atelier in Paris. In the next room, the beautiful stone altarpiece from the church of Plailly (Oise) shows along its borders the roses that were so frequently carved in ivory work of the period.

In contrast to the production of the French ateliers, or work of French inspiration, the art of Italian ivory-workers is also represented here: for instance, the large picture *(12),* which has a border of *certosina* and has a number of different scenes, which is displayed next to the cabinet. This is a characteristic example of the Embriachi style, but the work has been considerably modified.

On the west wall, to the left and in the centre, there are a few more works from the XIVth century, including a very beautiful St. John the Evangelist in marble *(13);* it is framed between two groups of choir-stalls *(14)* from the end of the XIVth-century.

43

16   3   11

Statues from Burgundy have been grouped around stand II: a figure of St. Anthony *(15)*, the Virgin from the château of Saint-Apollinaire *(16)* near Dijon, that of Plombières *(17)* and a St. James as a pilgrim *(18)* which closely resembles one from Semur in the Louvre; by their solid appearance, their shortened proportions and the weight of the clothes they are wearing they show how the Burgundian "image-makers" of the XVth-century interpreted and continued the lesson taught by the great sculptor Claus Sluter.

Coming back to stand I, some of the most important works in the museum are grouped in front of it: to the right, an admirable little statue of a female saint *(19)*, a French work from the beginning of the XVth-century; in the centre is the *Pieta (20)* that was acquired from the Hospice de Tarascon at the end of the XIXth-century. This picture, which is a primitive of the School of Provence, is a mid-XVth-century work. It is none other than the altarpiece of "Our Lord in the Arms of Our Lady" mentioned in 1457 in the inventory of the château of Tarascon; at this date it was "new" and was hung in the "new room of the Queen", Jeanne de Laval, second wife of King René.

At the end of the west wall we come to art from more northern latitudes: from the Low Countries and Germany, and also from Spain insofar as it is derivative of this. The altar screen of the abbey of Averbode

13

20

27

(Belgium), one of those large assemblages of painted and gilded wood *(21)* which were the speciality of the Antwerp ateliers, shows a rare subject: the *Mass of St. Gregory* together with the *Meeting of Abraham and Melchisedech* and also *The Last Supper*. It is also rare because we know both its creator and its date: Jean de Molder, 1513. Close by is a bust-reliquary in wood *(22)*, which probably is the work of Cologne ateliers. The small altarpiece *(23)* that follows is a work that is precious both for its painted panels and for its sculpture, which portrays the *Lamentation Over The Dead Christ*. This comes from the duchy of Clèves, and the village of Bethlehem in the adoration of the Magi can be identified as Kranenburg, a German town on the Dutch frontier. In the centre of the wall is a large Antwerp altar screen *(24)*; it is devoted, as was the custom in about 1520, to scenes of the Passion. To the left of it is a representation of the head of St. John The Baptist "in disco" *(25)*, probably from southern Germany. Above it is a beautiful statuette of St. Martha *(26)* which is also German; it was recently bequeathed by the Marquise de Flers; it was commissioned by a brotherhood of penitents who had themselves included wearing cowls. To the right is a moving death mask of Christ *(27)* carved in Spain, and above it a picture *(28)* which is part of a series now dispersed that is devoted to the legend of Géry, the apostle of Brussels. Lastly, at the end of the wall, is a pleasantly robust statue of a *Seated Virgin (29)* whose style clearly indicates that it came from the region of the lower Rhine.

46

36

38

33

21

29

23

Corbel from St. Jean-de-Latran (late XIVth century)

28

There are further examples of work from the northern schools on the east wall. Stand III contains statuettes mostly from Brussels or Antwerp; a small altarpiece of the Nativity *(30)*, which is very delicately sculpted, a St. Michael *(31)*, a curious Mary Magdelene *(32)* supporting the body of the dead Christ. To one side is a moving *Virgin Swooning (33)*, which was carved in Burgos after the Dutch style, and to the other a group that may be Spanish, showing the *Consecration of a Bishop (34)*. The two most beautiful works from the Brabant area in the museum have been displayed here. In the centre of the wall, a *Half-torso of the Virgin (35)* from Louvain, and a *St. Mary Magdelene (36)* from Brussels which is said to be a portrait of Mary of Burgundy, the daughter of Charles the Bold, which is set out separately in the middle of the room so that its elegant silhouette and picturesque hair style can be seen from all sides.

Stand IV is principally devoted to sculpture from Troyes, which was influenced by the Low Countries in the XVIth century. The statue of *St. Barbara (37)* has its double in the church of St. Urbain in Troyes; the *Marble Virgin (38)* which comes from Le Breuil (Marne), is already marked by the spirit of the Renaissance; it is the most remarkable piece in our series of works from the Champagne country, together with the charming *Mary Magdelene (39)* who kneels before the group *Crowning of the Virgin (40)* which is from Lorraine and is carved in a more angular style.

41

The end of the wall is devoted to the French northern provinces which too were subject to northern influence. The big altarpiece *(41)* from the Chapel of St. Eloi (Eure) is one of the most curious sculptures in our collections: it is in fact clay moulded on an original in the Brabant style. The two pictures either side of it were donated to Amiens Cathedral by the painters' guild at the beginning of the XVIth century; they show *The Coronation of David (42)* (with a beautiful *Pieta* on the other side) and also that of Louis XII *(43)*, which shows the ritual for the Royal coronation ceremonies in the Cathedral of Reims (we see in it figures presenting the sword and spurs that are still preserved in the Louvre today).

Similar works can be seen on the front of stand V: a picture from the Friary of Abbeville, showing the *Church of St. Wulfran (44)*, and the well-known *Virgin With Corn (45)* from the same place. Between them is a *St. Barbara* from Normandy, while to the right is another one *(46)*, in a simpler style. To the left, there is an elegant statuette which may be identified by the inscription carved on its base as a *St. Hubert (47)*, here shown in bishop's robes. In a niche, on the smaller side of the stand, a statue of a *Holy Woman (48)* is half-hidden; it comes from a group forming the *Laying in the Tomb*, and was never completed because it was placed on a bench behind the sarcophagous in which old men were preparing to bury the body of Christ, as is usual in groups of this kind. Lastly, on the other side, there are three groups in wood *(49)* from an altarpiece at Ourscamp (Oise) illustrating the curious legend of *"Santa Casa"* of Loretto.

43

50

St. John the Baptist — Italy (XVth century)

In cabinet 2 *(50)* there are some very beautiful works in a variety of techniques: schist moulds for casting bas-reliefs in wax, wooden caskets, statuettes in jet of St. James, of the kind that was commonly carved in Spain for the pilgrims going to Compostella, a XIVth-century German opening Virgin, and a small group with a curious subject: St. Luke painting the portrait of the Virgin; but the main work remains the Road to Calvary, one of the finest wooden sculptures carved in France at the beginning of the XVth century.

While leaving the Roman walls as bare as possible for their own intrinsic archeological value, the museum has used the niches cut in the east wall to house a *Sorrowing Virgin (51)* and a *St. John (52)*, between which is a beautiful *Crucifix (53)* from the Netherlands. On the opposite wall, which is less well preserved, tapestries have been hung: to the left, a small panel *(54)* showing the soul of *Honour (Decus)* being taken up to heaven by the three theological virtues (the Triumph of Decus is shown in room I). The museum was lucky enough to be able to acquire some years ago a large tapestry *(55)* showing the whole subject: by this juxtaposition, the visitor can appreciate the freedom left to the Medieval weavers in the interpretation of the cartoons they worked from. He will see that there are considerable variations, not only in the choice of the colours, but in the design itself.

ROOM IX

PAINTING AND SCULPTURE

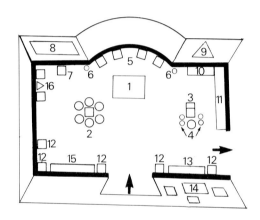

This room is devoted to works of the Romanesque epoch and to the early Gothic period. In the centre is a beautiful but tiny altar *(1)* in marble from the church of Montréjeau in the Pyrénées; either side of it are stands around which Romanesque capitals have been placed: to the left *(2)* six capitals originating from Catalonia.

The right-hand stand *(3)* is flanked by an admirable Burgundian *pilaster* from the abbey church of Cluny; it is surrounded by three capitals only, one of them decorated with acanthus leaves on Corinthian lines; the other two are double, and they used to surmount the twin columns of the Cloister of St. Denis. They are decorated with monsters carved in a fine and sensitive style *(4)*.

2

In the centre of the south wall, which is recessed like an apse, are the most famous statues in the museum; four (5) of the twelve apostles carved before 1248 for the Sainte-Chapelle that Saint Louis was having built for him in his Palais de la Cité, as a shrine for the relics of the Passion he had acquired from the Emperor of Constantinople. They were mutilated and decapitated in 1830; with the help of ancient drawings, it has been possible to fit the heads and bodies together again exactly as they were and so restore the statues to their original appearance. The work of a royal atelier, these statues have a grandeur of style that places them in the very first rank of sculpture during the century of Saint Louis.

On either side of this group are two small columns from the west facade of Saint-Denis (6) – that on the left restored in its central portion – whose rich decoration develops spirally up the shafts. To the left is one of the *Seated Virgins (7)* that were made in many examples in Auvergne over several centuries in imitation of the famous statue at Clermont. Above them is an altarpiece (8) painted in England in about 1300 and illustrating the *Life of the Virgin;* this work is a priceless possession for us since English primitives are rare and France possesses very few of them.

To the right, under a *Crucifixion (9)* painted in Germany in the XIVth-century, is a cabinet (10) containing objects from the VIIth-century up to the beginning of the XIVth; two Byzantine ivory plaques, possibly planed down during the iconoclastic period (the VIIIth-

51

century) and used on their reverse sides in the XIth or XIIth-century for a beautiful design of foliated scrolls and animals; a Byzantine *plaque in schist* showing two warrior saints; an ivory *tau* with tracery decorations which was discovered in 1799 in a tomb in Saint-Germain-des-Prés believed to be that of the Abbot Morard; a bishop's crook and a plaque both made in England using open-work of rare virtuosity; a *Seated Virgin*, hieratic and solemn, which is believed to be the work of XIIIth-century Paris ivory carvers; two *olifants* (hunting horns) made in southern Italy; and lastly, in the centre, a statue of a king in polychrome wood, carved in about 1300 – wrongly stated to have come from the great reliquaries of the Sainte-Chapelle, and considered without justification to portray Saint Louis.

The west wall is taken up on its full width by an *altar screen (11)* which used to be in the Chapel of the Virgin in the Church of Saint-Germer-de-Fly (Oise); it is characteristic of the Parisian art of the middle of the XIIIth-century. Above it are hung fragments from the great tympanum of the Last Judgment in Notre-Dame.

In front of the north wall stand three statues of apostles and one of Christ *(12)*, from the Church of Saint-Jacques-l'Hôpital in Paris; the finest one of this collection, that of St. James, the patron of the pilgrims who used to come to this sanctuary, is presented on the adjoining wall; these statues were carved between 1320 and 1325 by Robert de Lannoy and Guillaume de Nourriche. In the space between, on the left, is an altarpiece of the Passion *(13)* which is remarkable for its open-work arching and its pink and gold colours. Above are a few fragments of *mural paintings* taken from the refectory of Charlieu

10

14

(Loire) *(14);* the central scene shows King Boson of Burgundy presenting to St. Stephen the Abbey of Charlieu, which he had founded. On the other side is a gravestone, unfortunately incomplete, which shows the skill of the early tombstone engravers. Below it is a fine altarpiece from Plailly (Oise) *(15),* the grandeur of whose style has survived the mutilations it has suffered.

Another *engraved tombstone* on the east wall is even more interesting: it was for a child, but it does not bear his portrait, as was usual, but a beautiful silhouette of the Virgin, carrying the child Jesus on one hip as in the statues of the same period. Corner capitals, decorated with foliated scroll-work and animals, complete this corner of the room, while above the door is an arched marble *plaque* bearing a magnificently-worded inscription to an archbishop of Tyre. Lastly, a wooden *Calvary (16)* at the end of the eastern wall: the Virgin and St. John are represented in two powerfully expressive Italian XIIIth-century statues; the Christ, which is a little older, is of French XIIth-century worksmanship, possibly Burgundian; few examples of such work survive in French churches.

ROOM X

ARCHEOLOGY

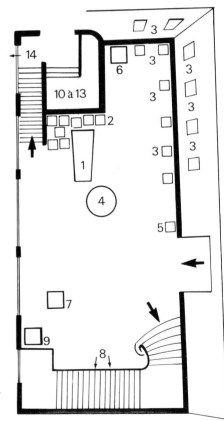

1

The oldest works in the museum have been collected together in this room. The pre-romanesque epoch is represented here by a fine *sarcophagus (1)* from the VIIth-century, decorated in champlevé with zig-zag moulding, arcades and a rosette. Eight capitals *(2)* stand at the top of the stairs leading down into the Thermal Baths; they are from Saint-Denis, and are carved in marble with a foliated design, and are probably the work of Pyrenean ateliers of the VIIth-century.

The essential element of the decoration of this room is XIth-century: placed against the Roman walls, which have been worn away by the centuries but whose structure remains visible, are twelve capitals *(3)* which are very early examples of the renaissance of stone sculpture that occurred in France from the year 1000 onwards. These heavy corbels, some of which are decorated with foliage in rough imitation of the ancient acanthus, and others are human or monstrous figures or showing scenes that have not yet been identified — with the exception of a Christ in Glory which is recognizable on one — come from the nave of the church of Saint-Germain-des-Prés in Paris; they were removed during the XIXth-century restoration and these "incunabula" of French Romanesque sculpture from the middle of the XIth century were reverently acquired by the museum.

In the centre of the room is a lavabo *(4)* or cistern from which water flowed into a basin for the ablutions of the monks before meals. This one is in marble and comes from the beginning of the XIIth-century; its only decoration is engaged columns with rough capitals.

Other works of more recent date, yet sufficiently monumental in character to match the still-crude style of these early sculptures, have been placed with them: a large statue of *a bishop (5)* from the XIIIth-century which according to a doubtful tradition is said to be the Saint Denis which used to dominate the facade of the famous abbey church of that name, a group of three Magi *(6)*, still magnificent despite the

2

3

3

7

mutilations they have suffered, from the north transept of Notre-Dame in Paris, and lastly another statue from the same cathedral, a mid-XIIIth-century Adam *(7)* that used to stand in the south transept.

Under the staircase leading to the first floor some romanesque capitals *(8)* have been placed; they are decorated, following the style of the period, with foliations or intertwining stems. One of them is storied and represents Original Sin: it probably comes from Burgundy.

To the right is a very fine early-XIIIth-century torso *(9)*, boldly and confidently sculpted: it is a fragment of one of the statues of apostles that used to decorate the central portal of Notre-Dame.

At the bottom of the staircase leading to the great Roman room we see a XIIIth-century Byzantine capital *(10)* showing three warrior saints; an epitaph *(11)*, dated 779, to the scholar Agnomarus, another (VIIIth-century) to Rotrude, and a third to Louis VI *(12)*, son of Philip I. Here also are some corbels and capitals *(13)* carved in the XIth century for the church of Deuil (Val-d'Oise) and in two vaults *(14)* are tombs that were formerly in the church of St. John at Rhodes. They were of five grand masters of the Order of the Hospitaliers of St. John (now known as the Order of Malta); that to the right contains an ancient sarcophagus, reused in the XIVth-century, for Robert de Julhiac (d.1376) and that of Jean-Baptiste des Ursins (d. 1476), as well as the tombstone of Dieudonné de Gozon (d. 1373); in that to the left are the recumbent tombs of Pierre de Corneillan (d. 1355) and Jacques de Milly (d. 1461) whose epitaph is accompanied by an inscription telling us that the young Prince of Antioch, Jean de Savoie (d. 1464) was buried "on the breast of the grand master".

GREAT ROMAN ROOM

5

6

Despite the ravages of the centuries, which have destroyed the rich wall facings and badly damaged parts of the masonry, the great room of the "Thermal Baths" remains France's most impressive relic of its period of Roman occupation.

Its enormous proportions – 65 feet long by 35 feet wide and 46 feet high under the vault, give a clear idea of the majestic scale on which the Romans conceived all their monuments, even those of a modest provincial town like Lutetia. The walls, in which are cut niches, arches and windows, are built of small cubical stones of very regular size, interspersed with courses of bricks which served as a key to the facing material, under which they were hidden. This method of building suggests a date at the end of the IInd-century A.D. The roof – a central groined arch with extensions of barrel vaulting on three sides – is the largest remaining in France from the Gallo-Roman era. The hanging gardens that were built above it during the Middle Ages have done nothing to weaken its solidity, and in the recent restoration the rendering, of which large patches can still be seen on the inner surface or "intrados", was consolidated.

With a room of such nobility and unique character, it is the architecture itself that should be presented, uncluttered by too many other works of art. The central area has therefore been kept quite empty to reveal the beauty of its proportions with only a few pieces of Gallo-Roman sculpture appropriate to the setting around the walls. There is a bull (1) found in the old church of Saint-Marcel, a frieze (2) which probably came from a tomb and shows a hare hunt, a fine Corinthian marble capital (3) found under the parvis of Notre-Dame, and three

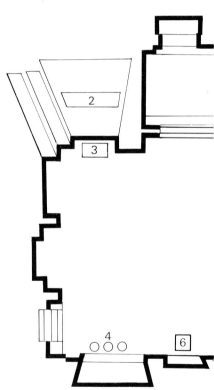

2

5

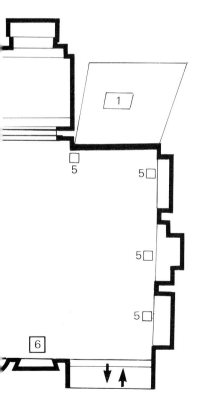

pillar shafts *(4)* found in the same place; they came from the old Merovingian cathedral of St. Stephen. The most important pieces from every point of view are the two series of blocks that were laid one on top of the other to form pillars such as those still existing at Mainz. There are firstly five blocks *(5)* – two of them make up a complete base – found in 1711 under the cathedral of Notre-Dame and representing both Roman and Gallic divinities: Mars, Venus, Fortuna, Mercury, Castor and Pollux, Cernunnos (the god with the deer's antlers), Smertrios, Jupiter, Vulcan, Esus, Tarvos trigaranus (the bull with the three cranes); and on the last block are six armed men, probably the "nautes du Parisis" (Seine boatmen), for it was they who erected this pillar in honour of Jupiter in the reign of Tiberius (14-37 A.D.), as we can see from the dedicatory inscription, which reads:

TIB (ERIO) CAESARE AUG (USTO) IOVI OPTUMO MAXSUMO S (ACRUM) NAUTAE PARISIACI PUBLICE POSIERUNT.

It is probable that the baths themselves were constructed by this guild of "nautes", who owned the monopoly of navigation on the Seine and of trade in arms; proof of this is said to lie in the carving of prows of ships loaded with arms on two surviving corbels at the spring of the great vault.

Three other later blocks, dating only from the IInd-century A.D., were discovered under the Church of Saint-Landry, in the Ile de la Cité *(6)*. The best conserved of them shows three divinities, Venus or Diana holding a torch, Vulcan and Mars, all carved in an admirable free style.

57

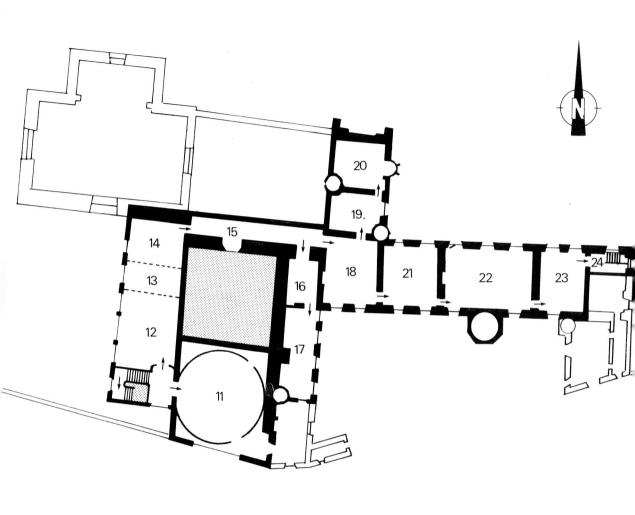

PLAN OF THE FIRST FLOOR

ROOM XI

THE LADY WITH THE UNICORN

3

The tapestry set of the Lady with the Unicorn is without doubt one of the finest works of art that survives from the Middle Ages. For more than a century, it has attracted to the Cluny Museum visitors from all over the world, who have come to pay it a fully-justified tribute. Such is the charm and poetry it exudes, the visitor has no difficulty in believing all the picturesque legends that have developed around it.

Its recent history has done nothing to attenuate the mystery that surrounds it. It was a famous writer, George Sand, who first brought it to popular notice. She was the first, in 1844, to draw attention to these tapestries, which she found in the Château de Boussac, hanging in the rooms of the sub-prefect. Shortly beforehand Prosper Mérimée, Inspector of Historical Monuments, had reported to his superiors the deplorable state of this hanging, and suggested that it should be acquired. To no effect, since it was not until 1883 that negotiations were successfully concluded and the Cluny Museum was able to purchase it. In the meantime, even the most serious of scholars had indulged themselves in wild flights of imagination about this work: the legends had appeared. The profusion of crescents in these tapestries had suggested a mythical idea of the East, and the presence of the young woman suggested slighted love. These two elements in combination evoked the memory of Zizim, an oriental prince who was held prisoner at Bourganeuf, near Boussac. It was thought that the prince, who had been expelled from his country and was languishing in grief, could have had it woven for his lady love. Since then, this error has been corrected and the theory of Prince Zizim has been abandoned, but the idea has persisted that the tapestry set was associated, because of the presence six times repeated of a young lady, with an engagement or marriage.

Analysis of the heraldry and of the subject matter completely rebuts these different hypotheses. The coats of arms — gules, a band azur with three crescents of argent — have for many years now been identified as those of the Le Viste family, one of well-known lawyers

1

2

originating from Lyons. Very early, this family moved to Paris and members of it assumed important functions in the royal administration and under the Parliament. Barthélémy was a counsellor in 1440, and his son Aymé succeeded him in this position in 1476 before his death in 1484, when he left two sons. The oldest, Jean, was appointed Maître des Requêtes in the Chambre des Requêtes (Magistrate in the Court of Appeal) and died without a male heir in 1500. His brother, Aubert, who had died some years earlier in 1493, left a son, Antoine, who was the last to bear the family's arms. As it was generally thought that the tapestry set had been woven as an engagement present, attempts were made to identify the lady in question. This theory must be finally abandoned, because the arms are undivided, and therefore those of a man. Otherwise the shield would have been "divided", with the arms of the husband to the right and to the left those of the bride's father. The only man in the Le Viste family who was a possible candidate, both for reasons of date and of inheritance that are too complex to set out here, is Jean Le Viste. This precious indication fixes the date at which the hangings were woven at between 1484, when Jean took the family arms on the death of his father, and 1500, the date of his own death.

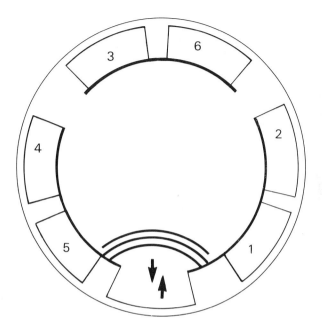

The subject matter is today understood, now that it has been shown that the set was complete with its six pieces. It was in this form that it was presented during the XVIIIth century at the Château de Boussac, when it was hanging there. Each of five of the tapestries illustrates one of the senses, a subject found in other mediaeval works:

Sight (1): the unicorn examines himself in a mirror held up to him by the young woman.

Hearing (2): the Lady plays a portable organ, whose bellows are worked by her servant.

Taste (3): the young woman chooses a delicacy from a bowl while the parakeet holds a sweet in his claws and a monkey, in the lower part of tapestry, is putting another in his mouth.

Smell (4): the Lady is making a garland of carnations, while the monkey is sniffing a flower that he has filched from the basket.

Touch (5): the young woman delicately holds the unicorn's horn with her left hand.

3

The sixth piece *(6)*, which shows the Lady standing in front of a pavilion whose flaps open widely to form a majestic frame, remained for many years without explanation. Despite what has generally been accepted, she is not picking out a necklace from the casket held to her by her servant, but she is placing it there, holding it in a cloth after having undone it from her neck. This is not then choosing the jewels, but taking off the jewels. The inscription woven at the top of the pavilion "A mon seul désir", when associated with this gesture, finds its explanation while at the same time giving meaning to the scene. It may be compared with the *"Liberum arbitrium"* (Free choice) of the ancient philosophers who saw in it the disposition in us to want to act aright, but which is taken away from us by the passions, i.e. the submission to our senses. This could appear to be a fragile interpretation if it were not confirmed by another example, also supplied in the form of tapestry. The Cardinal of La Mark owned, among his rich collections, a tapestry set in six pieces that bore the title of *Los Sentidos*. Five of them illustrated the five senses and the sixth bore the inscription *Liberum arbitrium*.

5

4

Another reading of this Cluny tapestry set is provided by the heraldry.
The number of times that the arms of Jean Le Viste are repeated
demands some explanation. They appear as many as four times in
Smell and *Taste*. Furthermore, the lances that carry banners and stan-
dards are fighting weapons with a sharpened iron. The tent in the
sixth piece is a form of pavilion that was more common at the time
on battlefields than in daily life. Jean Le Viste thus manifested his
pretensions to nobility, which were in fact to be disappointed, by
associating his arms with a pacific and profane allegory. In his will,
he went so far as to ask to be portrayed in a stained-glass window
of the chapel in his mansion "as a knight, wearing armour". This
lawyer, who reached the top of his profession and — a supreme honour,
this — was to be buried in the Chapelle des Célestins in Paris, ardently
hoped, like many others of his contemporaries who originated in
the provinces, to be ennobled. He was one of those whose hopes
were not rewarded.

6

The reputation of the "Lady with the Unicorn" comes from its harmonious colour scheme. The number of tones is limited, and are used always in shading to portray the great variety of elements in the subject-matter. These limited resources are sufficient to create a result of the highest poetical grace and charm.

The rounded "island" which serves as the ground for the scene portrayed is of dark blue, and is dotted with flowery plants; whereas the background varies between red and pink and is scattered with picked flowering branches. This system was frequent in the Middle Ages, on the evidence of the texts in the absence of the tapestries themselves, which have all too often disappeared. This splendid decor shows off the elegance of the young woman who appears in different attitudes and costumes. Her splendid clothes and the precious jewels she wears make the work even more beautiful.

ROOM XII

ENAMELS

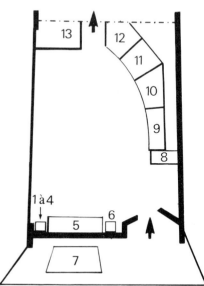

Enamel is a substance akin to crystal, and is coloured right through
with metallic oxides; it enables coloured decoration to be applied to
objects in gold, silver and copper. After firing at a high temperature
it becomes solid and highly resistant, and when polished has a rich
and brilliant appearance.

cabinet 1. GALLO-ROMAN AND BYZANTINE ENAMELS

The art of enamelling flourished throughout the Middle Ages, and is
deep-rooted in the history of France. Certain enamels *(1)* displayed
at the top of this cabinet, similar to those in the Museum of National
Antiquities at Saint-Germain-en-Laye, are late Roman dating back
to the IVth or Vth centuries A.D. These bronze "fibules" were decorated by the process known as "champlevé", i.e., the metal was recessed and filled (here without visible separations) with powdered enamel in different colours; these have with time become somewhat
devitrified and tarnished.

3

5

4

The byzantine enamels *(2)*, on the other hand, are nearly always "cloisonné" on gold, i.e., the recesses for the enamel are obtained by welding partitions of very fine gold strip to the surface. The minute detail of the work involved in making the countless and extremely delicate "cloisons" (partitions) on the enamels of the Eastern Empire is stupefying. Also, the work of Byzantine enamellers is often translucent, so that the gold (or sometimes silver) shines through; this gives these objects a precious splendour not found in Western enamels of the same period.

Cluny does not own masterpieces like the "Pala d'Oro" in St. Mark's, Venice or the "staurothèques" or reliquaries of the True Cross, like those in the church of the Holy Cross in Poitiers and at Limburg-on-Lahn; there is however here a beautiful griffon *(3)* with a gold base, and the figure of an angel both of which may date from the Xth or XIth century, the period when byzantine enamelling was at the height of its glory. There are also larger objects : a *plaque (4)* dotted with tiny stylized palm leaves of admirable workmanship which came from the Khakouli tryptich, and a prophylactic medallion decorated with a Gorgon's head and a Greek inscription .

ALTAR PIECE FROM THE MEUSE REGION *(5)*

The Rhineland, with Cologne as its centre, and the region of the middle Meuse — the former principality of Liège — formed the principal area for enamelling on copper in the XIIth century.

The altar piece, which was acquired at Coblenz during the Revolutionary Wars, comes from the abbey of Stavelot in Belgium. It was commissioned in the middle of the XIIth century by the abbot Wibald, and as in the great reliquaries of Meuse origin its enamelled parts are few: only the haloes, which are incidentally later additions, and the arch from which the bust of Christ emerges are decorated in enamel. The work is essentially in gold; the figures, in chased and

6

gilded copper, are very akin to those attributed to Godefroy de Huy, for example on the St. Heribert reliquary at Deutz.

cabinet 2 — ENAMELS OF THE MEUSE AND RHINELAND AREAS *(6)*

The goldsmiths and enamellers of the Meuse region were especially active in the middle and second half of the XIIth century. In imitation of the byzantine "cloisonné" enamels on gold, they used to recess and gild the copper base and only enamel the figures. Even the heads are usually recessed and engraved.

The small plaque, decorated with the busts of three prophets, *Isaiah, Jeremiah and Ezekiel,* with haloes, recalls the work of Godefroy de Huy, with its vigorously-drawn faces and hair encrusted with enamel on a background of gilded copper. The round plaque showing the *Adoration of the Magi* has been attributed to Lorraine.

8

"Champlevé" enamelling, which was much esteemed at Cologne, flourished east of the Rhine. In this area, the process usually used was the reverse of the above: the figures are recessed and engraved and it is the background that is enamelled. The two plaques of the *Wise Virgins* and *Foolish Virgins* may be of Westphalian origin, while the semicircular one showing the *Crucifixion* on a background of lapis lazuli blue with gilded copper studs is akin to a whole group of works probably made at Hildesheim or Brunswick.

A Brussels tapestry *(7)* from the beginning of the XVIth century has been hung on the upper part of the wall. It illustrates a mediaeval legend that was very popular at the time, that of the *Sibyl of Tibur showing the Virgin and Child* to the Emperor Augustus, who had come to consult her to find out who would rule over the world after himself.

8

9

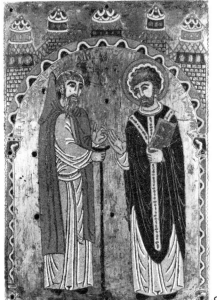

8

9

cabinet 3 — THE BEGINNINGS OF ENAMELLING IN SOUTHERN EUROPE *(8)*

At the end of the XIIth century, there was a considerable development of "champlevé" enamelling on both sides of the Pyrenees. There was no particular centre; thus an atelier was set up at Conques in the first half of the XIIIth century, and it is from here that the embossed cross probably originates. However the superb Christ in Majesty from the former Spitzer collection, which is one of a pair with a plaque showing the Crucifixion in the Valencia de Don Juan Institute in Madrid, is of Spanish origin. The technique is very distinctive — intentionally-numerous cloisons to replace colour shading — and similar to that of the front of the Silos tomb, which is now in the museum at Burgos. It is a mid-XIIth-century early example of the technique of inlaid heads.

The two plaques of the *Adoration of the Magi* and the *Conversation between St. Stephen of Muret and his disciple Hugues Lacert* — which is identified by an inscription in the Southern French dialect — are incunabula by Limoges enamellers who were soon to make a speciality of this; they come from the altar at Grandmont, near Limoges, and date from shortly after 1189, the date when the saint was canonized.

9

9

cabinet 4 — ENAMELWARE FROM LIMOGES

Two beautiful copper plates have been hung on the right-hand side of the first cabinet: a Flagellation and a Last Supper. They belong to a series, now dispersed in private or public collections. They are quite large and of exceptional quality.

The cabinet contains one of the richest and most varied existing collections of Limoges enamelware, whose period was from the end of the XIIth to the beginning of the XIVth centuries. At the end of the XIIth, the Limoges enamellers remained faithful to the technique of enamelled figures on a background of copper with vermiculated decoration (9). The two small fragmentary reliquaries in the first tier are good examples of this technique, which is admirable for the fineness of its incision and the beauty of its enamels. One of them even has inlaid figures. The plaque from the reliquary of St. Francis of Assisi, which is quadrifoil in shape, like the stemmed phylactery in the Louvre to which it is closely related, shows very similar technique, but it is not at all certain that it comes from Limoges. Very probably it was made in Italy, shortly after 1228, the date of the saint's canonization.

9

Later, Limoges adopted a different technique: the figures are no longer enamelled. They are now inlaid, or sometimes recessed with an incised decoration to show bodies and clothes, or in a mixture of the methods. The head may be stamped or cast and inlaid, while the body is recessed. The enamelled background of this beautiful blue enamel, which helped to establish Limoges' fame, is decorated with rosettes, foliations and fleurons in polychrome, or even with very elegantly-drawn Arabic letters. This production was exceedingly varied: certain figures are in very low relief like the St.

9

10

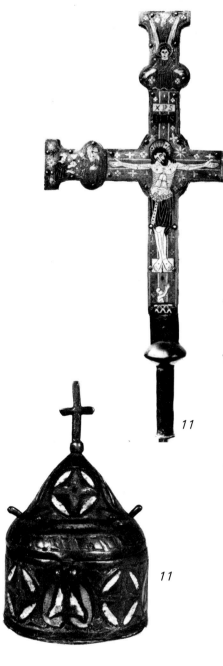

11

11

Paul (?) of the curved plaque, or in very high relief like those on the plaque that once was on the reliquary of St. Geoffroy from the church of Le Chalard (Haute-Vienne). Some plaques are so large that they must have come from altar pieces.

The small reliquary of St. Thomas-à-Becket, Archbishop of Canterbury, shows his murder and burial; the quality of its drawing and the beauty of its enamels make it a great masterpiece.

The second tier *(10)* contains a selection of religious objects, of which Limoges made a speciality: there is an incense spoon, which has today lost its enamel; a eucharistic dove, which used to be hung up and contained the Host; and above it is a suspended crown. This one comes from the treasure of Cherves (Charente). Incense-boats, candle-sticks and censers were made almost industrially, and were supplied to churches that could not afford objects in precious metal.

The third tier *(11)* contains a rich collection of pyxes, in which the Host was placed. They show a great variety of decoration. There is also a very beautiful double-sided cross, which has been recently acquired and came from the abbey of Bonneval (Aveyron): on one side it shows Christ in Majesty surrounded by the evangelists with their symbols, and on the other Christ on the Cross, with the Virgin, St. John, the Church and the Synagogue. By its colour choice and the presence of stars it belongs to a group including also the plaque of St. Francis, whose origin is probably Italian. This collection is completed by some reliquaries of rare beauty. That of a martyr, as yet unidentified, has engraved figures that are not inlaid, like those of the martyrdom of St. Sebastian and of Christ's Childhood; their execution is very fine.

11

11

The relics of St. Fausta lay until 1247 in the abbey of Solignac, when
they were transferred to the abbey of La Prée, in the Berry province.
The two shrines here in which they were placed come from this
abbey, and show two different techniques: the smaller has figures
in appliqué, whereas the other is merely engraved with very elon-
gated and finely-reproduced figures.

The fourth tier *(12)* contains the extraordinary head-reliquary from
the Homberg collection. One of Limoges' specialities was without
doubt bishops' crooks, of which more than two hundred examples
have been listed. Their coiled heads are decorated with scenes
like the Archangel St. Michael fighting the dragon, or the Childhood of Christ. One of the most beautiful of these comes from
Carcassonne. It has a widely-opened flower in admirable enamel
work.

12

The four bowls here are of a type known as "gemellions". One (to the
left) has a spout which was used to pour water into another. The
heraldic decoration or scenes on the umbo suggest that their purpose
was usually secular.

cabinet 5 — XIVth AND XVth-CENTURY ENAMELWARE *(13)*

This cabinet contains enamels from all periods whose origin is not
always known for sure. In imitation of Limoges, ateliers sprang up
all over Europe, and their work is sometimes not easy to identify;
the specialists do not always agree on the origin of a piece.

The copper plaque, decorated with enamel, of the old man Simeon
with St. Peter — identified by inscriptions — is an older work,
XIIth century, and German.

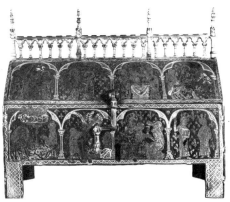

13

13

The delicate reliquary of the Life of the Virgin, on which engraved scenes picked out in red or white enamel are recessed into backgrounds of blue enamel, is probably French. The two XVth-century messenger boxes, also French, have unfortunately lost their enamel; the smaller of the two bears the arms of the Dukes of Burgundy, and the second those of Jean de Dargies, who died in 1409.

The casket of St. Claire on which are engraved scenes against a blue background, and also the very beautiful incense-boat, are Italian; the lid of the latter is decorated with an Annunciation, which is engraved and enamelled in red against a black blackground.

In the XIVth century there appeared a new technique known as "basse taille", which immediately became very popular. Translucent enamel was laid over a background of incised and engraved silver which showed through the vitrified layer. The artisan needed great skill in applying the enamel, and in practice it proved not very stable. The examples shown in the upper right-hand part are evidence of this. The enamel has often fallen off leaving backgrounds engraved with great delicacy. When it still remains the effect is one of rare beauty, with shading that recalls painting technique.

ROOM XIII

OBJECTS IN PRECIOUS METAL

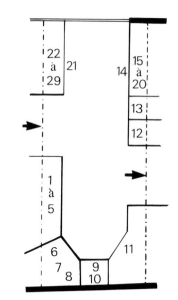

Objects were made in precious metal at all ages and by all civilizations. For obvious reasons — destruction, alteration, even economic — not many have survived.

cabinet 1 — GALLIC AND BARBARIAN JEWELLERY

The civilization of Gaul, of which few traces remain in France, is however richly represented in this field. Excavations, very often at random, have revealed jewellery of which a varied collection is preserved either at Cluny or in the Medals Section of the Bibliothèque Nationale and the Museum of National Antiquities at Saint-Germain-en-Laye.

The chain of six unequal rings *(1)* was found in 1844 in a tomb in the forest of Carnoët (Finistere) along with other less precious objects that are today at Saint-Germain. The spiral bracelet *(2)* comes from a sarcophagus found in the valley of the Ariège. A large treasure, probably hidden by a Gallic goldsmith during a period of strife, was discovered at Saint-Marc-le-Blanc (Ille-et-Vilaine) near Rennes in 1856. It included raw ingots and jewellery in a barely-started state which have not been preserved; the Cluny Museum was only able to acquire finished pieces: two rings and seven bracelets.

The spiral torque *(3)* with a hook at each end was found in a clay pot which was dug up in 1854 in the commune of Cessons (Ille-et-Vilaine).

The two finest objects in this cabinet — two torques, one a rope of four striated strands *(4)* and the other of heavy braid ending in a hook *(5)* — were discovered in 1866 at Montgobert (Aisne) on an uncultivated site belonging to Louis de Cambacérès, who donated them to the museum.

5

4

11

11

9

cabinet 2 — MEROVINGIAN JEWELLERY AND PRECIOUS OBJECTS

Merovingian art was largely confined to work in precious metals, usually for personal ornament or on soldiers' armour. The bridge-shaped bronze clasp *(6)* and the two small silver appliques with tracery decoration *(7)* come from Saint-Denis. The two digitate fibulae *(8)* were found in Paris at the place were the Lobau barracks now stands.

cabinet 3 — THE CROWNS OF GUARRAZAR

The Visigoth crowns discovered in the XIXth century at la Fuente de Guarrazar, near Toledo, form one of the most important of the "Barbarian" treasures that survive. Fourteen small crowns were found in 1858 by a French officer who was excavating on a site belonging to him; they were sent by him to the Madrid Mint where they were immediately melted down into ingots. Further excavation some time later on the same site revealed eight more crowns, which were bought by the Cluny Museum in 1859. A third excavation in 1860-61 brought to light several other crowns: the Museum acquired one, and the others were kept by Spain and placed in the Madrid Armeria, from which they were stolen in 1920. During the last World War, an "exchange" took place between the French State and the Spanish government, as a result of which Cluny was deprived of six of the nine crowns it had legally acquired. They are now in the Madrid Archeological Museum. They include the finest of all, which bears the name Receswinthe. Cluny still has the R in the form of a pendant; it is in the centre of the cabinet. The cross belongs to a crown that is now in Madrid, while that of the lattice-work crown is missing *(9)*.

The beauty of the Receswinthe crown, which is formed of a wide gold band decorated-with large sapphires and pearls, made it the centrepiece of the Cluny collection. It also offered the advantage of putting a date to the others. Reces winthe was associated to the throne by his father in 649; he succeeded him in 653 and died in 672. This piece was made during the period when King Dagobert's goldsmith was producing his masterpieces.

These objects were originally votive crowns suspended by small chains over the altar. A cross was attached in the middle. The band could be solid like that of the largest crown, decorated with stones and pearls and with sapphire drops hanging around it, or in openwork like the two others with a decoration of arcades or gold rods.

The large crown still has its cross, on which is an inscription that has not yet been satisfactorily explained:
IN DEI NOMINE OFFERET SONNICA
SANCTE MARIE IN SORBALES
Nothing is known of Sonnica, or of the church to which he donated this crown *(10)*.

cabinet 4 — BARBARIAN ART *(11)*

The pieces grouped here are on the whole contemporary with those in cabinet 2, but differ from them in that they are in gold (two Merovingian and one Byzantine *rings),* in glass (a *necklace, large pearl-drops,* a *pendant)* or — and this is the case of the *fibules,* the *pin,* the *plaques* and the *buckles* — decorated with red, green and white glasswork, and especially with garnets, the favourite stone of the Merovingian jewellery craftsmen.

10

13

cabinet 5 — THE COLMAR TREASURE *(12)*

In May 1853, a collection of jewellery was found in the thickness of a wall in the Rue des Juifs, Colmar. The numerous coins found with it suggest that it dates from the early XIVth century. One of the rings, in gold and red enamel, is considered to be a Jewish engagement ring, because of the Hebrew characters inscribed on the six faces of the pyramidical setting.

cabinet 6 — THE GOLDEN ROSE OF BASLE *(13)*

In this cabinet is an object of the greatest delicacy: the golden rose from the treasure of Basle cathedral.

It is well known that, towards Eastertide, the Popes were in the habit of presenting a small golden rose-tree to persons of high rank they wished to honour, queens, princesses or abbesses, for example. The treasure of Anne of Brittany contains a piece similar to this, described as "une rouse d'or autreffoiz envoyée par ung pape, au bout de laquelle a ung saphir" (a rose of gold formerly sent by a pope, at the end of which is a sapphire).

This custom, which has persisted to the present day, is very ancient, but the golden roses that have been preserved are nearly all of recent centuries. The one in Cluny seems to be the oldest known. We do not know its origin, or consequently its exact date. One tradition, which cannot be accepted as historical fact, has it that this rose was given to a bishop of Basle by Pope Clement V (1305-1314), and that it had been made by an Italian goldsmith in Avignon. However the filigree knot is earlier, and may be early XIIIth-century. At the beginning of the XIVth, three escutcheons bearing the arms of the von Aarburg family were added to the stem. Sold in 1834 with the treasure of Basle cathedral, the rose was given to Cluny Museum in 1854 by Colonel Theubert, to express his

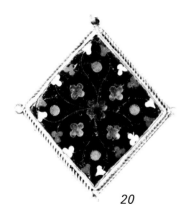

20   19

22

thanks to it for having acquired the gold altar front from the same treasure (room XIX).

cabinet 7 — XIVth- AND XVth-CENTURY JEWELLERY

Every century has had its jewellery, and ancient civilizations have left us examples of theirs in their tombs. Practically nothing survives from the XIth, XIIth and XIIIth centuries. It was only in the XIVth that we find an extraordinary wealth of precious objects, due to the enrichment of a new social class, and to the very luxurious tastes and strong influence of the aristocrats close to the throne. Unfortunately the finest examples have disappeared, and only the contemporary documents give us some idea of how splendid they must have been. But the few articles assembled in this cabinet will be enough to suggest the heights attained by this art, which was to reach its greatest achievement in the XIVth and XVth centuries *(14)*.

There were ornamental clasps in every kind of shape: one here is octagonal with stones on a high mounting *(15)*, while another *(16)* is hexagonal and simpler. The third is in fact a tiny reliquary *(17)*: the pin on its face was intended for fixing a thorn for Christ's crown, while the spaces around held other relics identified by inscriptions. Lastly, there is another round clasp *(18)*, on which large cabochons surround a beautiful translucent enamel.

With the XIVth century there appeared a new kind of enamel-work which is described in the texts as "plique" or "plithe" enamel.

24

80

This is in fact a resurgence of the byzantine technique of cloisonné on gold. Paris was soon to make a speciality of it, and precious objects in this style, both for civil and religious use, were soon to be found all over Europe. The two little enamels — one octagonal *(19)* and the other diamond-shaped *(20)* — were donated by Marquet de Vasselot, former curator of the Museum, and the rings on them suggest that they were designed to be sewn onto garments. They are traditionally attributed to Guillaume Julien, one of the leading goldsmiths of the early XIVth century, whose atelier was on the Grand Pont (main bridge) in Paris.

cabinet 8 — GLYPTICS

Classical antiquity was skilled in the technique of engraving on precious stones, which came to be known as glyptics. In the Middle Ages, the craftsmen usually did no more than remount stones from the classical period, cameos and intaglios *(21)*.

26

The two lioness heads *(22)*, which were found in a tomb on the banks of the Rhine together with a very beautiful figure in ivory (see the Treasure), were carved during the Vth century in the purest rock crystal; they probably served as arm-rests on a Consul's chair. The head of a child *(23)* is an ancient sapphirine chalcedony, and its XVth-century gold mounting bears the inscription "Mart (in) hanebo la donet". The tiny fish *(24)* and cicadas *(25)* were cut in rock crystal, jade or glass by Byzantine stone-cutters in the Vth and VIth centuries. The Virgin at Prayer *(26)*, the Christ in blood-red jasper *(27)* and the sapphirine St. Nicolas *(28)* are also of byzantine origin. The Christ on the Cross in red jasper *(29)* is probably a Western imitation of a byzantine cameo.

ROOM XIV

GOLD, SILVER AND GILT

The texts suggest that objects worked in metal were very common during the Middle Ages; they might be in gold, silver or even copper. War, revolution, changes in taste and damage have all contributed to their disappearance. The Museum has a very rich collection of them, varied both in date and in the material used.

cabinet 1 – PRE-ROMANESQUE AND ROMANESQUE WORK

The little silver reliquary in gilded silver *(1)* on a wooden core, which has a chasing of the Virgin and Child with St. Peter and St. Paul on either side, is similar in shape and technique to the shrine of St. Mommole at Saint-Benoît-sur-Loire, which was donated to the abbey in the VIIth century.

Mass was often celebrated during the Middle Ages on portable altars which were in fact altar stones mounted in metal. Cluny has three examples of these. The oldest is XIth-century German *(2)*: the serpentine marble is set into engraved and partially gilded silver plaques. On the front are portrayed the Sacrifice of Abraham, Melchisedech and Aaron. They appear around a Christ in Glory handing the keys to St. Peter and the book to St. Paul. On the underside is the Pascal Lamb surrounded by four Cardinal Virtues in half length: they are Justice, Prudence, Temperance and Strength. There is a magnificent inscription on the side.

This marvellous engraved plaque showing the Rivers of Paradise around the Pascal Lamb is engraved in copper *(3)*. Its fine and sensitive line suggests that it is by Godefroy de Huy, the great Meuse goldsmith of the mid-XIIth century. Another Meuse craftsman of the first half of the XIIIth century probably made the stemmed phylactery *(4)*. The front has a filigree decoration to which are attached mounted stones, while the inlaid reverse side shows Christ with the Virgin, St. John and the four apostles.

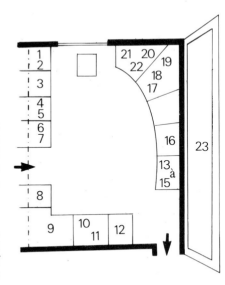

2

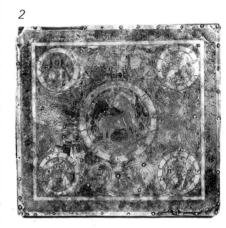

4

5

3

The evangeliary bookplate is Italian *(5)*. It is in silver, and partly gilded. The relief of the figures chased on it was help up by wax: traces of it can be seen where the metal has disappeared. In the centre, Christ hands over the keys to St. Peter and the book to St. Paul; on the edges, the presence of busts of saints, including the first two bishops of Novara, identifies the work as having been executed in this city during the first quarter of the XIIth century.

The last shelf is especially devoted to work from Northern France. The two magnificent reliquary crosses *(6 and 7)* with double horizontals, are contemporary one with the other; they have filigree chasing and stones in settings.

8

cabinet 2 — XIIIth-TO XVth-CENTURY WORK IN PRECIOUS METALS

In the XIIIth century, devotional objects became more diverse: the reliquaries often took the form of the fragment of body they contained. The monstrance appeared, revealing the relic or Host through a crystal mounted on a stem. The objects shown in this cabinet are of varying qualities and origins. The arm-reliquary *(8)* is a recent acquisition: it is in chased silver with a stamped border on which are enamelled fleurets. It is probably XIVth-century French.

The very fine XIVth-century silver processional cross *(9)*, with appliqué translucent enamels, shows a Christ on the Cross of great beauty, modelled in the round. It bears in several places the Barcelona hallmark BARCK, which occurs again on the box for holy oils which is on a stem and originally carried a small cross.

The little reliquary cross *(10)* decorated with cabochons is XIVth-century; it was mounted in 1454 on a base bearing the hallmark of Brioude. Above it is one of the greatest masterpieces of XIIth-century work in precious metal: the reliquary of the Sainte-Chapelle *(11)*, which was made to order by St. Louis to contain the relics of the holy martyrs of Beauvais, Lucien, Maxien and Julien. They are portrayed full-length with a feeling for relief that emphasizes the supremacy of sculpture at this period.

The magnificent double-sided processional cross *(12)* is a mid-XVth-century work from Siena. In the centre and on the arms are shown in very high relief: on the front, Christ on the Cross, the Virgin, St. John, St. Peter and Mary Magdalene; and on the back, Christ giving the blessing, surrounded by the tétramorphe.

9

10

11

15

2

vitrine 3. L'ORFÈVRERIE DU XVᵉ SIÈCLE

La première travée présente un choix de reliquaires mettant en lumière le degré de virtuosité qu'atteignent les orfèvres en cette fin du Moyen Age. Les formes s'inspirent de l'architecture monumentale en exacerbant le goût des courbes et des contrecourbes, des pinacles accumulés et des clochetons. Pour rendre l'objet d'apparence plus légère, l'orfèvre n'hésite pas à multiplier les percements.

Au fond, deux reliquaires *(13)* dont l'un serait peut-être portugais du début du XVIᵉ siècle. Les deux longues châsses allemandes *(14)* posées sur quatre pieds encadrent une remarquable statuette de sainte Anne portant sur ses genoux à droite la Vierge et à gauche l'Enfant, qui tiennent une châsse *(15)*. La sainte, d'argent doré et peint, est assise sur une chaise d'argent surmontée d'un dais. Au revers une longue inscription enseigne que le reliquaire a été exécuté pour le prix de cent florins en 1472 pour Anna Hofman, par Hans Greiff, orfèvre d'Ingolstadt.

La travée suivante contient des objets religieux courants en cette fin du Moyen Age. Le reliquaire d'argent *(16)* en forme de maison forte crénelée et cantonnée de tourelles a été restauré en 1612. Il était destiné à abriter un morceau du cilice de saint Louis de Toulouse.

La dernière travée de la vitrine contient un reliquaire en forme de livre *(17)*, une croix *(18)*, l'un et l'autre dus à un orfèvre allemand du XVᵉ siècle, deux croix-reliquaires, un plat d'argent en forme d'écuelle orné en son centre d'un médaillon autrefois émaillé, vraisemblablement d'origine française *(19)*. La corne à boire *(20)* alle-

22

23

century German drinking horn *(20)*, mounted on copper feet in the shape of eagles' claws, was for lay use. The gilded copper marten's head *(21)*, which still contains bones, was originally attached to the animal's fur, and was worn on the shoulder or at the waist.

The crossbow token is no less exceptional. Made in silver during the second half of the XVth century, it is attributed to the metal craftsman Israhel Van Meckenem. It is attached by a chain to a crown, and bears statuettes of the Virgin and Child and of the knight Hermès. The presence of this latter saint means that the work must have been executed at Warbeyen, near Cleves *(22)*.

On the north wall, over the cabinet, is hung the tapestry of the Prodigal Son *(23)*. It belonged to a set the other pieces of which have now been lost. The three scenes — the farewell, the departure, and the return — appear in arcades of which only the pillars remain. Their décor is already Renaissance, as are also the costumes; they situate the work in the first quarter of the XVIth century. The mille-fleurs design at the bottom of the piece merge upwards into a hilly landscape on which appear palaces, castles and genre scenes.

CORRIDOR XV

LIFE IN THE MIDDLE AGES

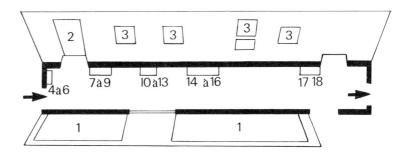

In this long dark corridor have been exhibited, on the south wall, a group of wood carvings *(1)*, together with the officiating priest's stall from the Picardy chapel. This building, which was consecrated in 1506, used to be in the Rue du Fouarre. Opposite it is a door *(2)* which is an early example of Renaissance style in Paris. Its match with the flamboyant style is as subtle as in the Augerolles screen.

A recently-installed series of stained glass panels *(3)* is a precious survival of this art form, dating from the end of the first third of the XIIIth century, shortly before the emergence of the Paris style of the 1240 s. Their range of colours is very rich — blues, purples, pinks, clear yellows and whites — and creates extremely subtle harmonies. Before the Revolution, this glass was in the windows of the abbey church of Gercy (Essonne), from which also comes the head of the reclining statue of Jeanne of Toulouse (Room II).

TABLEWARE

Two silver bowls found at Gaillon are XIVth-century. One is chased and has an enamelled medallion in the centre *(4)*. The chopping knife *(5)* is dated about 1500; it has a wooden handle and silver ferrule, engraved with an inscription, and its rectangular shape is because it was used for serving meat. Other metal objects — the goblet, the spoons in gilded copper, bronze or box-wood with a silver handle — illustrate the extreme variety of the domestic utensils that existed. The small cup *(6)* in grained wood is also trimmed with silver.

THE TOILETTE

The craftsmen of the Middle Ages used to add sumptuous decoration to mirrors *(7)*, which were simple sheets of polished metal. They

8

9

l'étranger. La valve *(8)* du début du XIVe siècle figurant un roi et une reine assis entourés de leurs enfants est vraisemblablement d'origine royale.

Plus rare encore est le peigne de buis *(9)*, marqueté et incrusté d'os dont certains éléments sont teintés de vert. Il porte sur l'une et l'autre face une plaque d'argent présentant les armes de Marguerite de Flandre, femme de Philippe le Hardi, morte en 1405, et son chiffre.

LE CHEVAL

L'importance que le cheval tenait dans la vie explique le nombre d'objets qui lui sont consacrés, depuis l'étrier *(10)* découvert à Elbeuf jusqu'au mors *(11)* magnifique, probablement exécuté à Limoges au XIIIe siècle, en passant par cette pièce *(12)* qui servait à nettoyer le sabot des chevaux. Les annelets volants *(13)* souvent aux armes du propriétaire garnissaient housses et harnais. Montés sur charnières, ils battaient l'un contre l'autre faisant office de cliquetis. Les carrefours, servant de point de rencontre entre les harnais, étaient souvent décorés avec soin.

L'ÉCRITURE

Au Moyen Age, on écrivait sur parchemin *(14)*, peau de mouton, de chèvre ou de veau spécialement traitée à cet effet. L'écriture a considérablement évolué au cours des siècles depuis la caroline qui apparaît à la fin du VIIIe siècle, inventée pour réagir contre la graphie mérovingienne devenue illisible, jusqu'à la cursive du XVIe siècle qui devint si difficile à déchiffrer qu'il fallut une nouvelle réaction. Mais seuls les textes importants étaient écrits sur de tels supports, en raison de son prix de revient très coûteux.

18

17

LE LIVRE

Il s'agissait en fait de manuscrit écrit et enluminé à la main sur parchemin ou velin, dont les reliures étaient très soignées. Certaines de ces reliures sont de véritables chefs-d'œuvre de l'orfèvrerie, qui peuvent enchâsser une plaque d'ivoire particulièrement précieuse ; d'autres sont d'émaillerie, de cuir doré ou estampé. Par mesure de sécurité et pour éviter les vols, le livre était souvent accroché au pupitre par une chaîne *(15),* comme on le voit ici.

LES SCEAUX

Le sceau était le moyen de valider un acte d'une personne physique ou d'une personne morale. Des matrices *(16),* dont on trouve ici quelques exemples, portent gravé en creux le décor inversé qui s'imprimait sur la cire chaude. Le sceau en navette de Marguerite de Constantinople, comtesse de Flandre (1244-1280) figurée debout entre deux lions rampants est de cire verte comme le magnifique sceau de majesté de Philippe le Bel. Quant au sceau équestre de Guillaume Ier de Hainaut, il est de cire rouge comme celui de Robert, duc de Bar (1352-1411).

LES JEUX

Au centre de cette vitrine, posée sur un très beau coffre de la fin du XVe siècle, aux armes de la famille Chambellan, à Dijon, se trouve une boîte à jeux *(17)* du XVe siècle, objet unique par sa qualité et sa rareté. Les tirettes développent les jeux divers de dames, de tric-trac, d'oie... Le bois est incrusté d'os teinté et d'ivoire. Autour ont été exposées quelques pièces d'échiquier d'os gravées de motifs géométriques, deux pions de dame en ivoire, les uns et les autres du XIIe siècle, et deux grands pions d'échecs figurant des personnages assis *(18)* et un gros dé.

ROOM XVI

STAINED GLASS

Probably the most original contribution to art of the Middle Ages was its stained glass. The Gothic period extended the windows of churches to such a degree that in some cases there was no stone wall left, but only immense surfaces of coloured glass through which filtered a shimmering pattern of light.

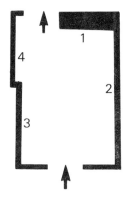

SOUTH WALL FACING THE ENTRANCE

The history of the stained-glass window in France begins really with the glasswork ordered by the abbot Suger for the choir of Saint-Denis and installed for its consecration on June 11th 1144. Cluny was lucky enough to acquire a remnant of this famous set, the subjects of which were prescribed by the abbot himself. It is a panel *(1)* showing the two disciples of St. Benoît looking at the path of light which had led their abbot up to heaven. In the bottom right-hand corner is a magnificent clasp in shimmering colours.

WEST WALL

The eight storied medallions *(2)* displayed on this wall are of various origins: they come from the Sainte-Chapelle, whose magnificent set, which still survives, dates from the middle of the XIIIth century, but they had been brought there in the course of the centuries and many of the pieces were originally elsewhere. One of these is the Resurrection of the Dead (top left), which is a beautiful piece of Paris stained glass from about 1200, and is remarkable for its blue background decorated with foliation and the vigorous drawing of the nudes. However two or three medallions are thought to have formed part of the original glass of the chapel of St. Louis, especially the one at lower right; its probable subject is the captive Samson turning the millstone. The medallions in the centre are in a much more delicate style, and testify to the sophistication that the art had attained at the end of the XIIIth century.

2

4

1

EAST WALL

The four large windows *(3)*, which were once in one of the chapels of the royal palace at Rouen, date from about 1260; they demonstrate the remarkable development of stained glass in the second half of the XIIIth and during the XIVth centuries. Colour is now only used in the centre of the window; the rest is patterned with foliations drawn in "grisaille". Four seated apostles are recognizable here: St. John, St. James the Elder with his shells, St. Peter and St. Paul. The beauty of the design, the richness of the colours and the accuracy of the expressions and gestures place these figures in the forefront of painting on glass of this period.

Next to these are three splendid panels *(4)*, which are earlier (around 1200) and come from Troyes cathedral. Two episodes from the legend of St. Nicolas are recognizable: the statue of the saint erected by a Jew to protect his house from thieves, the charity given by the saint to the father of three poor girls, and Christ attended by angels after the Temptation in the Desert.

SALLE XVII

LA CÉRAMIQUE

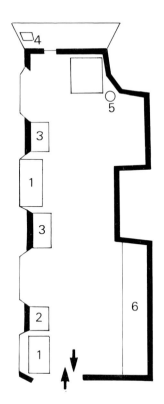

vitrines 1 et 4. LES CARREAUX

Il existe une variété assez étonnante de carreaux médiévaux *(1)* dont on trouvera, dans ces deux vitrines, des exemples qui s'échelonnent du XIIIe au XVe siècle. Certains seulement estampés de motifs géométriques ou héraldiques, d'autres au contraire incrustés de ces mêmes motifs mais aussi de scènes. D'autres ont été exécutés pour constituer des ensembles. Ils sont tous originaires du nord de la France, mais de régions différentes : le castillet, enfermé dans un carré posé sur la pointe qui s'enlève sur un fond sombre, provient du château de Caen. Les quatre fleurs de lys qui rayonnent autour d'un point central se trouvaient à Saint-Denis. Quelques-uns viennent de l'abbaye de Fontenay.

vitrine 2. LES POTERIES

Les quatre éléments de conduit de chaleur gallo-romain *(2)* ont été découverts lors des fouilles des Thermes de Cluny, en 1943.

Les autres pièces médiévales sont des poteries flammulées, c'est-à-dire que la poterie est seulement décorée de quelques traits de peinture rouge ou noire. Cette production d'usage courant, qui s'est étendue aux XIIe et XIIIe siècles, adoptait les formes les plus variées. Les traces qu'on remarque sur la panse de certaines d'entre elles indiquent qu'elles étaient funéraires. Disposées dans les tombes, elles contenaient quelques braises dont l'incandescence était ainsi assurée.

vitrine 3 et 5. LES POTERIES VERNISSEES

Les poteries vernissées *(3)* présentées dans ces deux vitrines ont été découvertes lors des travaux effectués à Paris, boulevard Saint-Michel, rue de la Harpe, à Saint-Jean-de-Latran, rue des Grès. Cette ville s'était spécialisée dans cette technique dès le XIIIe siècle, en utilisant les émaux verts, jaunes et bruns. Les formes variées et

1

3

4

3

recherchées, avec l'emploi de reliefs, soulignent qu'il s'agit d'une poterie supérieure à la poterie commune.

Dans la partie haute de la vitrine est exposé un magnifique plat qui porte en relief les instruments de la Passion, qui lui ont donné son nom. Une inscription le date de 1511 alors que l'emblématique est celle de Charles VIII, mort en 1498 et de sa femme Anne de Bretagne. Malgré cette différence de date, son authenticité ne peut plus être mise en doute depuis que des fragments semblables ont été découverts dans des fouilles, à Beauvais. Il apparaît comme le chef-d'œuvre des potiers du Beauvaisis.

A gauche de la porte est exposé un fragment de mosaïque (4) figurant une tête de jeune femme. Du XIIᵉ siècle, elle provient de Torcello, près de Venise.

La grande jarre (5) placée à proximité est un magnifique et rare exemple de la poterie vernissée espagnole.

CÉRAMIQUE HISPANO-MAURESQUE.

Le Musée de Cluny possède une des plus remarquables collections de céramique espagnole "à reflets métalliques" (6) qui soient au monde. Il s'agit de ces belles pièces fabriquées à Manisès, faubourg de Valence.

On peut admirer ici plusieurs pièces d'une insigne rareté, qui datent du début du XVᵉ siècle : au centre du dressoir, trois bassins creux à "bellières" — rassemblement unique, puisqu'on n'en connaît qu'un autre exemple à New York —, dont le décor de style persan, avec

6

Their decoration is in the Persian style, with an eight-pointed star, and is copied from XIVth-century Andalusian work; the colours, almost-violet blues associated with a deep ochre, are of great richness. Next are two large early-XVth-century medicinal pots, decorated in the same style but with more subdued blues. There is similar colouring on the *bowl* and *plate* either side of them; each of these has an escutcheon in the centre, with around it four segments of a circle in Arabic letters. A similar bowl in America helps us to date them at about 1430. It is a pity the visitor cannot see the reverse side, where there is a savage and proud heraldic eagle framed in light waving plant stems.

On the dresser to the left are displayed some fine pieces with ivy-leaf decoration: a *plate* and an *ewer*, on which this design is in a warm ochre colour, two *"albarelli"* where there is an alternance of ochre and blue, and especially a large and splendid *"winged"* vase, one of the principal pieces in the collection, on the bulge of which is a coat of arms with a lion of the type known as Florentine (there is in England a similar one with the arms of the Medici). Lastly, to the right on the dresser and wall are some pieces — *plates*, a *bowl* and a large cup — in blue parsley-leaf design. This design is one of the most delicate and attractive to come from Manises, where a great many similar objects were made from about 1430 up to the end of the century.

6

ROOM XVIII

SAINT-LUCIEN DE BEAUVAIS.

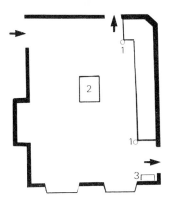

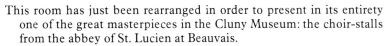

This room has just been rearranged in order to present in its entirety one of the great masterpieces in the Cluny Museum: the choir-stalls from the abbey of St. Lucien at Beauvais.

They are set up around three walls. Their history is too complex to be given here in detail; suffice it to say that the architect appointed in 1820 to restore the basilica of Saint-Denis bought them and installed them in the winter choir. They were partly dismantled in 1873 and put into store before being passed on to Cluny in 1889-1890. The first consignment only included two reveals (row-ends), some columns, and forty or so seat frames and misericords. Two other series have been added quite recently, the first purchased in 1970 and presented in Room XX, and the second recovered from Saint-Denis, dismantled, and included in the reconstituted set. The only modern elements are the base, the backs and the arm-rests with their fore-edges; the rest is of the period.

The two reveals (1) on the east wall and its north return are carved, to the north with St. Peter sending St. Lucien, St. Maxien and St. Julien to convert the inhabitants of the Beauvais district, and to the east with Antoine Du Bois, their abbot from 1492 to 1500, who kneels before his patron saint the hermit Antoine.

There is not much uniformity of style in the misericords as a whole, and account of this has been taken in the reconstitution. On the northern wall, the carver who was evidently influenced by the art of the north has portrayed scenes with complicated subjects, using sharp edges and broken folds. To the east, on the other hand, another artist of quite different training has preferred to render clowning scenes with greater elegance. These misericords, some of which devoted to trades are exhibited in Room XXIII, give an extraordinarily vivid picture of contemporary life.

1

3

Au centre de la pièce sur un pupitre octogonal *(2)*, ont été exposés
sur châssis tournant deux livres d'heures, l'un du début du XVᵉ siècle
et l'autre du milieu. Les marges sont ornées, comme il est de coutume
à l'époque, d'un décor filigrané. Des petites scènes illustrent les
travaux des mois mis en parallèle suivant la coutume médiévale avec
les signes du zodiaque.

A gauche, un précieux retable allemand *(3)* du début du XVIᵉ siècle
figure les scènes de la passion taillées dans le buis, s'enlevant sur
un fond de couleur. Sur les volets sont représentés saint Accursius
et sainte Catherine.

SALLE XIX

TRÉSOR

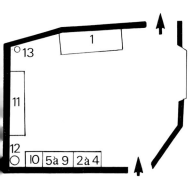

Dans cette salle qui jouxte la chapelle, on a rassemblé quelques-unes des pièces précieuses du musée, afin d'évoquer les riches trésors qui s'étaient constitués, au Moyen Age, auprès des églises de quelque importance et dont on peut encore se faire une idée à Conques, à Sens, à Aix-la-Chapelle, à Saint-Marc de Venise ou encore à Monza, près de Milan.

L'AUTEL D'OR DE BALE *(1)*.

La pièce maîtresse est l'autel d'or de Bâle, l'œuvre la plus rare et la plus précieuse du musée. Il s'agit d'une de ces "tables d'or" placées devant l'autel, que l'époque carolingienne et le XIe siècle avaient multipliées, mais qui, presque partout, ont été fondues. Aussi n'en reste-t-il plus que quatre dans le monde entier : l'incomparable "Paliotto" de Saint-Ambroise de Milan, la "Pala d'oro" de Saint-Marc de Venise, le devant d'autel de la cathédrale d'Aix-la-Chapelle et celui de la cathédrale de Bâle que le musée de Cluny a recueilli.

Chef-d'œuvre d'orfèvrerie, sans nul décor d'émail, il est fait de feuilles d'or battu appliquées sur une âme de bois et de cire. On reconnaît, debout sous des arcades et identifiés par des inscriptions, le Christ bénissant et tenant le globe du monde — *Rex regum et dominus dominantium* —, les trois archanges, saint Michel, Gabriel et Raphaël, et saint Benoît, abbé du Mont Cassin. Sur le fond, de riches rinceaux enserrent de leurs tiges ondulantes quatre petits médaillons où les vertus cardinales apparaissent en buste ; d'autres courent sur les bordures, s'épanouissent en feuilles découpées ou se nouent autour de figures animales.

Au terme des plus récentes recherches, l'"Autel" aurait été fait, dans les premières années du XIe siècle, par des orfèvres "lotharingiens", sur l'ordre de l'empereur Henri II, dit le Saint ou le Boiteux, qui s'est fait représenter avec sa femme, l'impératrice Cunégonde, prosternés

the feet of Christ. It is thought that it was intended for some Benedic-
tine monastery, which explains the choice of the persons represented.
But the emperor, in pressing need of money, probably caused it to be
placed in Basle cathedral as a surety, and it was there, before the
high altar, when the cathedral was consecrated in 1019. During the
religious wars of the XVIth century it was hidden away in the vaults
of the cathedral. It was sold in 1836 by the canton of Basle with part
of the treasure. Cluny acquired it in 1854.

IVORIES

In a large cabinet are assembled the oldest ivories the museum owns,
together with some objects in plate and a wooden plaque which is
just as precious.

Ist tier to the left:

On the left is a large figure *(2)* cut in ivory — one of the largest that exist —
of Ariadne, which as one of a pair with a Dionysus probably came
from a consular chair or folding seat. It was discovered in the tomb
of a consul near Trier, together with the two heads in rock crystal
which were probably the arm-rests. She is standing, crowned by two
cupids, and holds a thyrsis and a cup. On either side of her are a satyr
and a child. The loose and flowing style of the draperies suggests an
Alexandrine work of about 500 AD.

On their appointment, the imperial consuls were in the habit of sending
their friends ivory diptychs *(3)* for use as notebooks, with their por-
traits on the external faces. Aerobinbus, who was consul in Constantinople in 506, is shown seated, bearing the emblems of his office
and holding in his right hand the "mappa" with which he gave the
signal for the games, shown below, to commence. In his left hand
he holds the sceptre ending with the eagle and topped with a representation of the reigning emperor.

The exact origin of the other ivories in this tier has still not been ascertained. The St. Menas, the folds of whose robe are somewhat crisply rendered, is thought by some to be an Alexandrine work of about 600 AD, while others bring it forward to the XIth century. The plaque *(4)* showing Christ crowning the emperor Othon II (972-983) is the work of a Western artist who copied a byzantine ivory.

2nd tier:

In the centre is one of the great masterpieces of hellenistic art: the diptych volet intended to commemorate the marriage of a couple from the Nicomachi and Symmachori families, families of senators that were linked twice, in 392-394 and 401. The second volet in the pair is in the Victoria and Albert Museum, London. The Cluny one has suffered from having spent some time in a well, where it was discovered. Before the Revolution it had been remounted in a reliquary in the abbey church of Montier-en-Der (Haute-Marne). A priestess of Ceres with robes in soft folds stands near the altar holding two inverted torches *(5)*. In the centre of the cabinet is an extraordinary Crucifixion *(6)*. This early-XIIth-century German work, which is as precious as an ivory, is carved in a wood that has acquired a beautiful brown patina.

Four works in precious metal give contrast to these striking ivories. There is a XIIIth-century byzantine cross in silver with three horizontals, on a wooden core. There is a book-cover whose early-XIIIth-century plates, decorated with filigree and cabochons, each contains a preciously-preserved ivory plaque of an earlier period. One shows a standing Virgin surrounded with busts of apostles, of byzantine inspiration, and the other a very sensitive Carolingian Crucifixion *(7)*.

5

99

8

9

Le coffret-reliquaire *(8)* présente le même parti : les plaques de cristal de roche taillées à l'époque fatimide (vers 1020) de quadrupèdes affrontés, ont été enchâssées au XIIIᵉ siècle, dans une monture dont les filigranes sont rehaussés de pierres. Il provient de la Cathédrale de Moutiers en Tarentaise. Enfin, déployant superbement ses ailes sur une plaque d'argent gravée de flammes et inscrit entre des croissants, l'aigle reliquaire est en fait un fermail. Perles, pierres, émaux rehaussent encore la beauté de cet objet. Il s'agit en fait de l'aigle de saint Wenceslas, ancêtre des rois de Bohême et il aurait été exécuté dans ce pays dans le troisième quart du XIVᵉ siècle *(9)*.

10

A l'exception du Christ en majesté byzantin du XIᵉ siècle auquel un artiste occidental du XIᵉ ou XIIᵉ siècle a ajouté deux plaques portant les symboles évangéliques, la troisième travée de cette vitrine réunit un certain nombre d'ivoires occidentaux *(10)*. Le saint Paul taillé dans une mince plaque d'ivoire qui a souffert, appartient à un groupe d'œuvres produites dans la seconde moitié du VIᵉ siècle ou au VIIᵉ. L'apôtre qui tient un volume, est à rapprocher de certains ivoires exécutés sous Charles le Chauve.

C'est à un artiste colonais que l'on doit la Crucifixion : le Christ en croix vêtu d'une longue robe plaquée par le vent, se tord dans un étonnant mouvement ; — à un ivoirier d'Echternach le saint Paul creusé dans une niche qui forme ombre, le visage griffé de rides profondes. Le coffret-reliquaire, plus tardif, présente sous des arcades dont le fond est formé de plaques d'or, des personnages hiératiques qu'identifient des inscriptions. Il appartient à une série d'œuvres produites à Cologne au début du XIIIᵉ siècle.

LES VÊTEMENTS LITURGIQUES.

Dans cette vitrine ont été réunis quelques rares vêtements liturgiques, et des ivoires ; à gauche, la crosse de saint Martin *(11)*. La volute

12

10

rated with an Adoration of the Magi, was mounted in the XIIIth century on a box-wood staff carved with thirty scenes from the Life of Christ. There are also two caskets, one probably XIIth-century byzantine with an animal design in ivory and wood marquetry, and the other made by Arab craftsmen installed in Sicily.

In the centre of the cabinet is the silk tunic discovered in the tomb of Pierre de Courpalay († 1334) at Saint-Germain-des-Prés; on either side are two velvet chasubles onto which older embroideries have been sewn. To the right is a magnificent Crucifixion on a blue background, surmounted by a Swooning Virgin; it is early XVth-century. To the left is a Crucifixion from the beginning of the XVIth century, together with St. John and the Virgin in the lower part.

A green bishop's stocking decorated with gazelles and birds comes from the tomb of Arnaud de Via († 1355). The artisan from Lucca who wove it has included threads of gold. The precious bishop's glove is also from the tomb of Pierre de Courpalay.

A magnificent Cufic inscription in long blue letters was found in the tomb of a bishop of Bayonne.

The moving bust-reliquary (12) which is Italian XVth-century, still contains the skull of St. Mabille, one of the eleven thousand virgins martyred at Cologne. It is carved in wood, and decorated with delicate polychrome which has survived.

The "unicorn's horn" (13) is in fact a narwhal's tusk, the exaggerated canine tooth of a whale that lives in northern waters. The Middle Ages attributed extraordinary virtues to these objects and kept them as precious relics in their treasures. This one comes from Saint-Denis.

ROOM XX

THE CHAPEL

The chapel, which is built over a vaulted passage joining a courtyard of the Roman Baths and the Gothic garden, is one of the most elegant pieces of architecture that survive from the end of the Middle Ages. The extravagances of the flamboyant style are here finely tempered; the design of this little chapel approaches perfection with its flawless proportions and exquisite decoration.

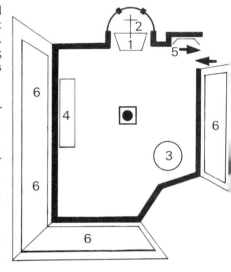

Time has scarcely wrought any damage to it: the twelve statues of different members of the Amboise family that were disposed on the upper part of the walls disappeared during the Revolution, but the corbels, decorated with vine-stocks and oak branches, and the finely-chiselled canopies still bear witness to the precision and artistry of the man who carved them. Below are twelve *consecration crosses* which were painted for the dedication, according to liturgical custom. A delicate network of drip-moulding fillets covers the surface of the vault, or at least that part of it that remains visible between the abundance of spreading arches that carry its weight, fanning out from the top of a slim pillar in the centre of the room. The suspended keystones that marked the intersections of the arches have unfortunately disappeared. To the east is a small apse which is corbelled out over a pillar, where the altar used to be; in the buttress to the right an opening has been intentionally cut to allow the abbot to see the officiating priest from the preceding room and so follow the Mass without leaving his warm room. On the vault of this absidal extension there are still XVth-century sculptures: the Father giving the blessing, Christ on the Cross, angels flying in the sky or carrying the Instruments of the Passion. The Renaissance made its contribution to the decoration of the oratory, with the painted figures of Mary Salome and Mary Jacobi, lamenting the tragedy of Calvary, on either side of the altar. At the other end of the chapel, in one of the corners, is the top of a small spiral staircase whose entrance is concealed behind a screen of rounded stone, pierced through with wide fillets which adorn this part of the room with their delicate grace.

To emphasize the sacred character of this room, in the absence of the altar, which has disappeared, an *altar front (1)* has been set up in the absidal extension. It shows four holy people under wide arcades: a bishop, a martyred deacon, St. Peter and St. Jerome; this fine work was found in the course of excavations when the Rue des Écoles was being cut through, i.e. on the very land owned by the abbots of Cluny at the time their residence was being built. On this simulated altar stands a large *cross (2)* of gilded and silvered copper; it is a relic from the church of the Grands Carmes, which stood near here in the Place Maubert.

A beautiful XIVth-century font *(3)* from the church of Embsen (Hanover) has also been set up here.

2

6

6

Against the north wall is the funeral effigy of Blanche de Champagne *(4),* the wife of John I Duke of Brittany (she died in 1283). This magnificent work, which is formed of copper sheet over a roughly carved wooden core, comes from the abbey of La Joie, near Hennebont (Morbihan).

To the right in an alcove is a *triptych (5),* painted in Germany; on the volets can be seen the donor and his family being presented by St. John the Baptist and a female saint, and in the centre is the *Miraculous Mass of St. Gregory.*

The story and legend of St. Stephen (6), a set of Gothic tapestries that are among the most famous in the museum, brings warmth with its bright blues, greens and iridescent reds to the stark bareness of the stone. It enhances the beauty of the building, which is at the same time a perfect setting for it, since these are religious tapestries, one of the "choir hangings" with which the sanctuaries of great churches were often decorated in the Middle Ages. This one was commissioned in about 1490 by Jean Baillet, bishop of Auxerre, and for nearly three centuries it decorated the choir of the cathedral in that city. Sold at the end of the XVIIIth century and again in 1880, it has now found a home, complete, in Cluny Museum. Some 140 feet long in all, the set is hung here in the chapel and the two adjoining rooms; in twenty-three tableaux it relates the story of St. Stephen, patron of Auxerre cathedral, and the legend of his relics. The visitor will find the first scenes displayed in the chapel (starting on the back wall); they continue in Room XIX and end in Room XVIII. In this way he will be able to follow, scene by scene, one of those curious "Lives of the Saints" that inspired Jacques de Voragine's XIIIth-century *Légende Dorée,* and which helped sustain the passionate and somewhat credulous fervour of the Middle Ages.

4

ROOM XXI

COPPER AND BRONZE

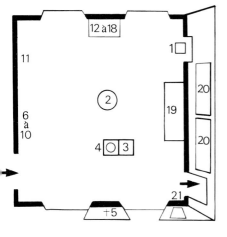

1

In the room have been assembled works in copper and bronze, i.e. foundry work. The ease with which copper can be extracted and processed explains its privileged role in all civilizations. Of low density, ductile and malleable, it is most often used in alloy form. Mixed with tin and zinc it gives bronze, and with zinc alone brass — to work in which alloy the town of Dinant, which made a speciality of it, gave the name of "dinanderie".

In an alcove cut out for it is a magnificent lectern *(1)* in the shape of an eagle, which comes from the church of St. Nicolas in Tournai. An inscription on its base relates that it was donated in 1383 by two wool merchants, Damians and Velaine.

On the display *(2)* in the middle of the room are some XVth-century works: two candlesticks, a ewer, and a Dutch Virgin and Child.

In the centre are two corn measures, the smaller *(3)* found at Puiseaux in the Loiret département being decorated with a frieze of men and women dancing; the second *(4)* comes from Milly and bears the names of the man who cast it, Roger d'Amiens, and of the man for whom it was cast.

On the courtyard-side wall is a Crucifixion *(5)* in gilded and painted copper; on the back is a hunting horn, the emblem of Antoine, the great bastard of Burgundy.

9

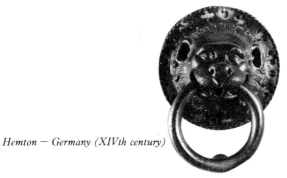

Hemton — Germany (XIVth century)

13

On the west wall is a dresser with various XVth-century objects: three offertory plates, *(6)*, two cooking-pots *(7)*, a pot for heating water *(8)* and a mortar surrounded by four "aquamaniles" *(9)*. These ewers, the oldest examples of which are XIIth-century, often take the shape of fantastic animals, such as here a griffon, a horse, and a unicorn *(10)*.

The cabinet *(11)* on one side displays a series of objects from different periods: candlesticks, a ewer, censers, perfume-burners, with at the top three offertory plates from the XVIth century.

In the cabinet to the north are a number of objects from shrines and reliquaries. Some particularly deserve attention: a very beautiful XIIth-century crucifix, which has developed a magnificent green patina from a long stay underground *(12)*, a crozier *(13)* of about 1200, whose scroll is of very pure design. Opposite is another crozier *(14)* decorated with the Pascal Lamb which is said to come from Clairvaux. There is also a XIVth-century angel *(15)*, which has suffered from the passage of time. Lastly we may mention a little column from a XIIth-century shrine *(16)*, a Christ and a Virgin *(17)* from the end of the Romanesque period and a Kiss of Peace *(18)*, dated 1468.

Above the recently-acquired choir-stalls *(19)* from St. Lucien-de-Beauvais are two large fragments from a hanging of the Life of the Virgin *(20)*, donated in memory of Jacques Bacri by Mme Bacri and her daughter Mme Saltiel. The presence to the left of Léon Conseil, Chancellor of Bayeux cathedral, accompanied by an abbot and their patron saints Exupéry and Paul, establishes that this was the set he donated to Bayeux cathedral in 1499. To the right are three scenes: the Annunciation, the Visitation, the Virgin and St. Joseph in the Holy House. ·

21

On the return wall is a picture *(21)* showing the Parable of Lazarus and the Rich Man painted on wood by a Paris artist in about 1420.

ROOM XXII

IRON AND ARMOURY

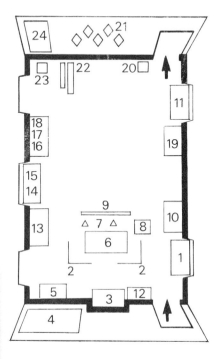

2

In view of the importance of iron in every civilization, it was natural to devote a room to it in a museum of the Middle Ages. This metal which, found in its natural state, lends itself readily thanks to its ductility and malleability to every kind of use and shape, also offers the advantage of welding itself easily provided the surfaces are cleared of the oxide layer produced by the fire. Constantly annealed and hammered at red heat, it can be decorated either by stamping (hot, with a die) or by filing.

One of the most original productions of the mediaeval ironsmiths were door irons (straps and grilles). In the flat cabinet (1) in front of the window are some stamped fragments from one of the doors of Notre Dame, from the early XIIIth century. Alongside, a strap of the same period has been remounted on a wood panel. The imagination of the artisans had free rein in the grilles, whose design lent itself to the most fantastic shapes. Two magnificent examples (2) from the XIIth century come from Saint-Denis, while the others are XIIIth to XVth century.

In the fireplace (3) which has the same origin as that in the Vie Seigneuriale tapestry, have been presented a mediaeval fire-back bearing royal arms, two fire-dogs, a pot-hook, a grill and a meat-hanger.

A mille-fleurs tapestry (4) placed over a XVth-century chest (5) evokes the art of forging, with Tubalcain who is said to have invented it, and that of weighing.

In the centre are certain objects that deserve attention. A very fine XIVth-century chest on feet, sheathed with iron plates held by stamped nails (6); two large ecclesiastical candlesticks (7), a folding desk (8) and especially some moulds for making sacramental wafers (9) from the XIVth, XVth and XVIth centuries. The most beautiful

9

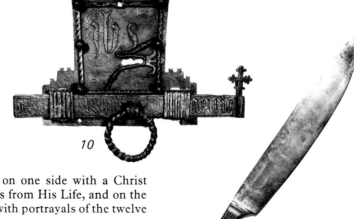

10

of these, circular in shape, is engraved on one side with a Christ giving the blessing surrounded by scenes from His Life, and on the other with a Christ showing his wounds with portrayals of the twelve apostles.

cabinet 1. LOCKS

A very large collection of locks *(10)*, bolts and other door fastenings from the last part of the Middle Ages shows how flamboyant decoration invaded all aspects of life. The hasps that concealed the keyhole have figures engraved on them. A very fine late-XVth-century bolt bears the inscription IHS, and next to it is a no-less surprising chest lock.

KEYS

The cabinet in front of the window demonstrates how keys *(11)* developed from the Gallo-Roman epoch up to the beginning of the XVIth century, and also shows the different types: lifting, full rotation and angular-movement keys.

KNIVES

A small cabinet contains some knives *(12)*, including a XIVth-century hunting knife, and two magnificent bread or meat knives, with rounded steel blades. The rarer of the two has a copper handle, engraved and enamelled with the arms of Philip the Good, Duke of Burgundy.

12

ARMS

The struggle for survival, with all the cruelty it implies, has dominated the history of man since his origins. To extend the action of his limbs, and also to protect them, man has used every kind of material: wood,

13

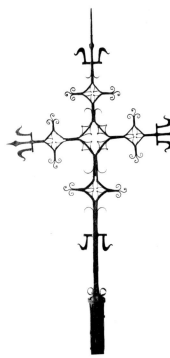

Cross (XVth century)

stone, and later bronze, iron and steel which being more flexible lent themselves to all purposes. The Middle Ages marked an important stage in this development with the appearance of armour, for foot and especially mounted soldiers. It was to change over time with a slowness that can be explained by its high cost. Most of the numerous coats of armour made have disappeared: war, time, rust and fashion have all contributed to this. To learn about the different types of armour we have to have recourse to illustrations, which are fortunately abundant.

cabinet 3.

Despite the wealth and diversity of its mediaeval collections, Cluny possessed no element of armour, with the exception of the *helmet vizor (13)* in the lower centre of the cabinet; note how the nose-piece is extended to make blows slide off, and how exceptionally large is the eye aperture, which must have given insufficient protection. This piece only came into the museum in 1909, after having been in the Carrand and Victor Gay collections; it is said to have been found on the field of Azincourt, and it appears to be contemporary with the famous battle in 1415.

Four helmets have been obligingly lent by the Musée de l'Armée; its rich collection in the Invalides includes, in addition to various types of helmet, other elements such as breastplates and gauntlets.

cabinet 4. In front of the centre window

Here there are two interesting though incomplete specimens of *brigandines*. This term describes a protective garment composed of iron scales riveted together to overlap and covered on the outside by velvet, fixed by nails that were usually gilded. The first *(14)* to the left, is a breastpiece showing the fabric trimming that is still fixed to the

iron armour; while the second *(15)* is probably a back-piece, and shows the iron scales, whose design is of great variety and subtlety. Between the two is exhibited an early-XVIth-century Italian gauntlet.

cabinet 5.

To the left are two swords *(16),* used by the Vikings before or a little after their establishment in Normandy in the Xth century, and a sword like those the Normans had when they conquered England in 1066; similar ones can be seen on the famous Bayeux embroidery.

On the right are three elegant XVth-century swords from the magnificent collection left to the museum in 1888 by count Édouard de Beaumont. One bears the arms (a serpent devouring a babe) of the Sforza family of Milan; the other, which is certainly German, was intended to be attached to the saddle horn *(17)*.

In the middle are various other arms *(18)*: a *mace* and a *fighting hammer* from the XVth century, and a *"broquel"*, a small round shield for foot soldiers. In the centre is a German sword from the second half of the XVth century, also from the É. de Beaumont collection. To establish a dynastic tradition an engraved and gilded decoration was added in the XVIth century: on the one side, a German inscription meaning "Tournament sword of the emperor Frederick, in the year of our Lord 1459"; and on the other, a portrait of this emperor, Frederick III, father-in-law of Marie of Burgundy.

18

On the floor is a large curved-bladed sword, known as a *"fauchon"* and used by foot soldiers; this one dates from the XIIIth century, and bears on its bronze pommel a heraldic "castille" in engraving and champlevé. It was found in 1861 during an excavation near the Pont-au-Change bridge.

cabinet 6. Facing the preceding one

21

The locksmiths used to make, in addition to the locks themselves, boxes or caskets, which were either entirely in metal, or in wood sometimes covered with leather or parchment and banded with iron. The latter may be formed, stamped or cut out.

Most of these *caskets (19)* are so similar in decoration that one might think they all came from the same centre. With their slightly domed lids, their heavy mouldings, their openwork plaques that seem to have been beaten, their flamboyant fenestrations around the lock, they are XVth-century (probably late). Their style may be compared with that of some of the door fastenings in the Hospice de Beaune (second half of the XVth century).

On the east wall, to the side, is a "maximilian" suit of armour of about 1520 *(20)*. With it is a large collection of targes and "pavis", wooden bucklers covered with leather or cloth. They come from Central Europe: Germany or Bohemia. Some of them are of remarkable quality, like the one in the centre decorated with David and Goliath *(21)*.

Below are two bombards *(22)* and a XIVth culverin, characteristic of the artillery pieces that appeared at the end of the Middle Ages. To one side is a wooden statue of St. George, appearing as an armed man of the XVth century *(23)*.

Lastly, a tapestry *(24)* of the *Return from the Hunt* shows a nobleman bringing a hare to a young woman.

ROOM XXIII

2

3

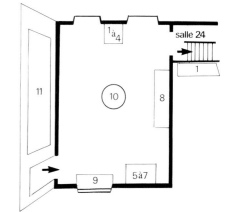

Tin and lead were frequently employed in the Middle Ages. They were used for everyday articles, as they were malleable and cheap. However these were fragile, which explains why so few have come down to us.

cabinet 1.

Here there are only objects in tin. An absolution cross *(1)* bearing an inscription with the name of Edelbert, who died at Archiac during the reign of Philip I, is a unique piece found in a tomb. The XIIth-century chalice *(2)* is just as rare. The XIIIth-century ampulla *(3)*, which was found in the Seine, was used by pilgrims to hold holy water or oil. The XIVth-century salt cellar *(4)*, showing the Annunciation, is similar to another in the Kunstgewerbe Museum in Berlin. There are a number of openwork plaques, which were used for making caskets. And lastly, the Museum owns a large collection of these rounded or closed cups, whose precise purpose is not known.

cabinet 2. COUNTERS AND TOYS

Most of the objects exposed here come from the Gay or Forgeais collections, the latter assembled from pieces found in the bed of the Seine during dredging operations between 1848 and 1860. The most remarkable are the series of children's toys *(5)*.

Political badges *(6)* visibly showed the factions to which their bearers belonged — the Burgundy faction with the St. Andrew's cross, the Dauphin's with the dolphin, or the English faction.

8

9

11

6

There is an extraordinary collection of "méreaux", or guild counters *(7)*, bearing the emblems of the different trades.

cabinet 3. PILGRIMAGE INSIGNIA

Pilgrimage insignia *(8)* were sold near the place of pilgrimage, and were attached to the hat or garments. Most of the great French pilgrimages, Le Puy, Boulogne, Le Mont Saint-Michel, are represented here by these little figurines, some of which have been executed with great art.

MOULDS

In front of the window have been displayed some moulds, some of which were used for casting metal. The purpose of the round German mould in slate, which is a masterpiece for the quality of its execution, is not fully understood *(9)*.

In the middle of the room is a lead font *(10)*.

Also displayed in this room are some misericords from the choir-stalls of Saint-Lucien de Beauvais, portraying trades, and a very large early-XVIth-century tapestry illustrating the story of David: to the right, Nebuchadnezzar prepares to slaughter the wise men of the kingdom; to the left, David is explaining to him the dream of the colossus with feet of clay, suggested at top left.

ROOM XXIV

In the staircase that leads down to the last room has been hung a tapestry *(1)* devoted to hunting and pastoral scenes. It is early XVIth-century.

A number of Jewish devotional objects are provisionally displayed in this room. Two extremely fine and rare pieces deserve special attention: a Tabernacle of the Law *(2)*, dated by the inscription 1471, and an early-XVIth-century pulpit *(3)*. There are some smaller objects in the two cabinets on the west wall *(5)*.

Under the staircase is a cabinet containing a series of illuminations, which have come to Cluny torn out of their manuscripts *(4)*. They show how the miniature has evolved from the Romanesque era up to the XVIIth century. Two of them are early-XVIth-century and are attributed to a pupil of the Boucicaut Master; they show God the Father surrounded by the evangelical symbols and Christ on the cross, against a squared background. An illumination suggesting the month of August, bearing the arms of Claude Gouffier, contains a rare reproduction of a piece of Saint-Porchaire pottery. The Seven Rondeaux of the Virtues of Louise of Savoy extol the mother of François I in acrostic verses.

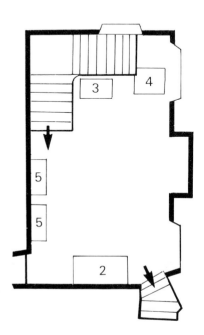

2

4

4

mise en page : Atelier Philippe Gentil
composition : Typelec
photogravure : Intergraphic
impression : Imprimerie Mame